Medical Wider Reading
UK Medical Application Guide

Why should you bother with wider medical reading before you even get to medical school?

Medical school applicants have to demonstrate excellent insight into the medical profession. This is achieved in part, by doing wider reading and familiarising yourself with subjects such as medical ethics, scientific research and topical healthcare-related issues. This background knowledge helps you to contextualize your decision to pursue a career in medicine; it will be of specific use during medical work experience, volunteering placements and when you come to write your personal statement. You can also easily refer back to this book when preparing for your medical school interviews. In short, medical wider reading can make you a more informed, prepared and ultimately more convincing applicant to medical school!

Why should you read our 'Medical Wider Reading' book?

Our Mentors have put together this comprehensive knowledge and skills guide, specifically to help highly motivated medical school applicants to develop a competitive edge. You should view this book as a foundation text, and supplement it with rapidly evolving topical resources, such as the Mentor Magazine and relevant healthcare sections of the media. *Medical Wider Reading* is great to refer back to when double-checking things such as, tricky ethical principles, scientific research concepts or detailed transferable skill breakdowns. In addition to all this, you can add your own notes from your own experiences, creating an ultimate, personalized resource for medical school applications!

Need more help? Medic Mentor is here to support you!

Medic Mentor is a social enterprise comprised of doctors, medical students and many other healthcare professionals. We provide useful resources, mentoring and opportunities for aspiring healthcare students. We understand how challenging and confusing medical applications can be, simply because we have all been there...many of us more than once!

Find out more at **www.medicmentor.co.uk**

Title: *Medical Wider Reading*

Authors: *Dhakshana Sivayoganathan, Iain Kennedy, Ciaran Kennedy*

Editors: *Iain Kennedy, Akash Bhalla*

Publication date: *June 2018, 1st Edition, Paperback*

Publisher: *Medic Mentor Publishing Group*

ISBN: 978-0-9569720-9-5

Medic Mentor Motivating Medical Minds, is a registered trademark.
Printed by Medic Mentor Publishing Group, a subsidiary of Medic Mentor Ltd.
Website: www.medicmentor.co.uk.

Purchasing any of the Medic Mentor Medical Application Guides and/or books, does not guarantee a place at medical school and it is the individual student's responsibility to submit an application via UCAS. All advice and information provided by Medic Mentor Ltd is believed to be true and accurate at the date of publication. The company cannot accept any legal responsibility or liability for any errors or omissions made. Medic Mentor Ltd makes every reasonable effort to ensure content accuracy in all of its resources. Due to the dynamic nature of medical school applications however, institutions are constantly updating their course details. To read the full disclaimer visit www.medicmentor.co.uk/disclaimer.

Kind regards, Medic Mentor Publishing Team.

Dedication

This book is dedicated to every aspiring medical student. Medic Mentor is here for you from your first step, throughout medical school and on the journey to an exciting career as a medical professional.

Medic Mentor - Motivating Medical Minds.

Contents

# Chapter 1: A Concise History of Medicine & Surgery

Mentor's Tip

*In this chapter, the mentors will introduce you to a selection of notable figures and events throughout the history of medicine and surgery. This is neither an exhaustive list, nor must you learn all the details included. We have offered insight into a wide range of discoveries over an extensive period of time. This will give you the opportunity to identify the contributions to the medico-surgical universe that you find most interesting. These topics can be used in your personal statements to demonstrate wider reading and breadth of knowledge. This chapter will also be useful when answering interview questions regarding influential figures and events in medical history. You should prepare a subject that personally interests you, rather than regurgitating a list of generic answers. You can find more details about the sorts of questions interviewers might ask in Medic Mentor's **Interview Skills Checklist** (available from www.medicmentor.co.uk).*

Hippocrates

Hippocrates was an Ancient Greek physician born in Kos around 460 BC. He has often been identified as 'the father of western medicine', with his work well ingrained in modern medical practice. He established medicine as a field in its own right, dissociating it from other disciplines such as philosophy. We can see glimpses of his contribution to the medical establishment through the Hippocratic Oath and its subsequent revisions including the Declaration of Geneva. These oaths are taken by doctors across the United States and stipulate ethical standards for them to maintain. In the United Kingdom, the General Medical Council produced a document entitled, Good Medical Practice. This document contains guidelines that embody many concepts of the Hippocratic oath, such as working in the patient's best interest and the patient's right to confidentiality. These ethical principles are discussed in detail chapter three of this guide (medical ethics).

Hippocrates established the Hippocratic school of Medicine where he taught his students the concept of holistic medicine. This form of medical practice requires physicians to consider all the factors that may contribute to the patient's condition as a whole (e.g. physiological, psychological, social, economic and cultural), rather than solely fixating on the pathological manifestations. Interestingly, this form of medical practice was abandoned in the dark ages but has recently seen a revival. Furthermore, holistic treatment is considered a fundamental principle of many alternative and complementary therapies.

Hippocrates published his work, '*On Airs, Waters and Places*', which attempted to establish a relationship between disease and the environment. This was one of the first notable examples of an observational study and deviated from the traditional unsubstantiated ideology, that disease was a result of divine intervention. This scientific approach to medicine bears a resemblance to the 'evidence-based medicine' (EBM) movement, of recent years. Principally, Hippocratic medicine focused upon the healing powers of nature and required physicians above all else, to do no harm.

Galen

Following on from Hippocrates was Galen; a Greek physician during the Roman Empire (AD 129 – 216). Galen contributed to medical history through developing our understanding of the circulatory system and human anatomy. Many of Galen's anatomical findings were based on his dissections of animals and were not necessarily applicable to humans. However, as Galen was considered a supreme authority on medicine (and because the church subsequently prohibited human dissection), many of his ideas remained unchallenged for centuries.

Galen also championed many concepts of Hippocratic medicine and brought them to the attention of the world: 'humourism' was one such concept that Galen supported. This was a belief that all disease was derived from an imbalance of certain bodily fluids known as the, 'four humours' (see figure 1). These humours were associated with the four elements and temperaments, which supposedly dictated your personality type. It was believed that the variable excretion of these bodily fluids was the body's mechanism of returning to humoural equilibrium - and therefore health.

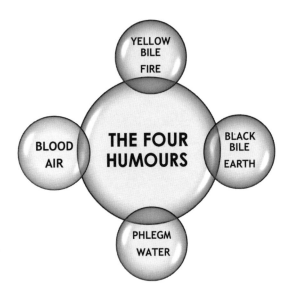

Figure 1: The Four Humours

Blood, yellow bile, black bile and phlegm were associated with the four elements: air, fire, earth and water respectively.

Galen furthered this topic by asserting that a functional body relied upon pneuma, or the body's spirit, rather than just a balance of the humours. Humourism was maintained as a central concept to western medicine until the 19th century when it was replaced with more scientifically founded concepts.

Marcus Vitruvius Pollio

Throughout the Roman era there was an awareness of the effect of the environment on health. The Romans attempted to reduce these effects through sanitation measures such as building aqueducts and sewers. A prominent example is the work of Marcus Vitruvius Pollio. He identified that a substantial number of men working in the lead foundries fell ill. He reasoned that lead was the cause of this illness. He then suggested that clay pipes should replace the lead pipes currently used for drinking water to prevent lead-associated ailment.

Sushruta

Elsewhere in the world, long before the time of Hippocrates or Galen, lived a man who would found the discipline today known as surgery. Sushruta was born in southern India (circa 1200 - 600 BC). During his time he produced the *Sushrut Samhita* – a medico-surgical textbook that received global recognition as a volume of excellence.

One of Sushruta's more noteworthy accomplishments was the successful implementation of the forehead flap rhinoplasty, which is still in use today in modern plastic surgery. This procedure was used to replace a missing nose; In ancient India, women accused of adultery could have their noses cut off. Clearly Sushruta was not dealing with the root of the problem here but his contribution to modern surgery is still felt through the ages.

The forehead flap rhinoplasty involved cutting a section of skin from the forehead. This flap would remain attached at a point (known as a pedicle), to maintain adequate blood supply to the skin. The flap would then be folded over into the shape of a nose and sutured onto the face to form a replacement nose.

Enter the Dark Ages

During the dark ages our understanding of medicine and surgery seemed to regress; triggered by the collapse of the Western Roman Empire, between the 4th and 5th century AD. Western Europe reverted to primitive methods of medical practice, composed of a blend of humourism, herbalism and religious healing – with a splash of the occult for good measure. The Church, being one of the only enduring bodies of influence, mediated this transition. It disseminated the notion that disease was God's punishment for sins and only resolved through prayer and repentance – instilling a sense of superstition to medical treatment. It was understood that the outcome of treatments depended more upon the religious beliefs of a patient and a physician, than on any empirical evidence. The Church considered Galen's work infallible, and so they forbade dissection of the human body, deeming it unnecessary.

Throughout this period, medicine was regarded as something for the rich and highly educated. The high levels of illiteracy amongst society and the relative inaccessibility of medical texts, eroded medical understanding. Consequently, many ideas of classical medicine, such as an appreciation for the need of hygiene and sanitation, seemed to have been washed away during the Middle Ages. These antique ideas were mainly kept alive by the Islamic Middle East. Islamic physicians such as Rhazes, Avicenna and Averroes, developed the findings of their Greek and Roman predecessors. Avicenna produced the Canon of Medicine, which fused the medical knowledge of the ancient Greeks with the current medical insights of the Islamic community.

Meanwhile in the West, physicians employed a variety of methods that today would be seen as cruel. They believed in the idea of bloodletting through leeches, to rebalance the humours. Trepanning (drilling a hole in the skull), was commonplace and believed to release the bad spirits, which supposedly caused disease. Cauterisation (burning body parts with heated metal), was also seen as an effective treatment. In general these methods were counterproductive and did more harm than good.

Astrology also played a significant role in medical practice. Doctors assessed the position of the moon during procedures and used a device called an almanac to gage the alignments of the stars, prior to making diagnoses. Many believed that disease was due to bad smells and the removal of smells would therefore resolve the disease. In fact, this idea would be carried on through to the 17th and 18th centuries, where plague doctors utilised beak-like masks filled with aromatic substances to protect them from these 'plague-inducing' smells. This is in line with the miasmic theory of disease, which is discussed later.

Surgeons, many of whom were butchers and barbers, were trained through apprenticeships rather than via formal education - unlike their distinguished physician counterparts. Surgery actually progressed during the Middle Ages, unlike medicine. Surgeons started using wine (as a primitive antiseptic), to prevent disease and using opium (as an anaesthetic) to prevent pain. However, as they lacked an understanding of microbiology, their operations often led to a high rate of infection and death. **John Arderne**, is a historical figure of note as he is often considered to be the father of English surgery. He developed a surgical management for anal fistulae, amongst other things.

Between 1346-53 AD, the Black Death would spread across Europe and killing millions; reducing England's population to a third of its original size. The Black Death was a bubonic plague (that affects the lymphatic system), caused by the bacteria *Yersinia pestis*. It was thought to be spread by the vector of fleas, which infested rats and were transported down the Silk Road by European traders. In response to this pandemic, 'plague doctors' emerged. These were often not properly trained physicians. Many used ineffective methods to treat plague, such as placing frogs on buboes (large swellings which often burst, oozing blood and pus).

Revitalising Health in the Renaissance

Until the renaissance period, anatomy was regarded as an unfavourable field; forming only a small portion of medicine. It was something for the barbers to toy with - not 'real' physicians. This started to change when academics took a greater interest in anatomy, sparked by the work of **Leonardo da Vinci,** whose detailed drawings on the human body surpassed any other work of that time. One prominent example of this work, was his drawing of a foetus in utero. Unfortunately, da Vinci's work was not published until long after his death and consequently did not have that great an impact on renaissance medicine.

Andreas Vesalius

Subsequently and independently, Andreas Vesalius (1514 – 1564 AD) revolutionised modern anatomy. Vesalius was a physician born in Brussels. He worked as the head of anatomy in Padua, Italy. His most prominent piece of work was the *De Humani Corporis Fabrica* (on the fabric of the human body). The 'Fabrica' contained the renowned 'muscle men' diagrams, which presented human bodies, stripped down to their musculature, in various animated positions. Vesalius questioned and opposed Galen's ideas on human anatomy. For example, Galen believed that the human liver had more lobes than it actually did from his studies on animals, and he also posited that blood passed through small holes in the heart from one side to the other, which Vesalius identified as anatomically incorrect.

Renaissance Medicine and Surgery

This would mark an era where medical practitioners would stop blindly following Galen's teachings and begin to review the work of the ancient Greeks and Romans critically; where the church's influence over medicine started to wane and public dissection in theatre became somewhat of a novelty. Furthermore, dissemination of knowledge greatly improved through the development of the printing press. As anatomy started to come into fashion, its discoveries trickled down into surgical practice. Traditionally, medieval wartime surgery was characterised by limb amputation followed by cauterisation with hot iron (and later boiling oil), to seal the wound. **Ambroise Paré,** a French wartime surgeon during the renaissance thought this practice was unnecessarily brutal and ineffective with many of his patient's dying after cauterization. Paré replaced cauterising oil with his own tincture of egg yolk, turpentine and rose oil; finding that his tincture often had better outcomes. Later Paré developed a technique cause ligation where he would clamp the arteries using his on invention, the 'Crow's Beak' (a precursor to the modern haemostat or artery clamp); tying off the vessels using silk thread rather than cauterising them. Technically, this was a better method, however other surgeons were slow to adopt his idea, partially due to the high death rate from infection. Equally, physiology developed through **William Harvey**'s explanation of the circulatory system, which amended Galen's many inaccuracies.

The Age of Enlightenment

Towards the end of the Renaissance period began the Scientific Revolution; part of the 'Age of Enlightenment'. This was an era where logic and reasoning were valued over traditionalism. It saw advances in the natural sciences such as chemistry and physics, which in turn translated into scientific medicine (e.g. through the invention of the microscope). During this period of industrialisation, there was a reduction in the quality of life and the life expectancy of many, due to factors such as the pollutants of industry, poor living conditions and various infectious diseases such as cholera (more on this later).

Thomas Sydenham

Often referred to as the 'English Hippocrates', Thomas Sydenham discovered that Peruvian bark (which contains the molecule Quinine) was useful in treating certain fevers. This illness-treatment relationship had a level of specificity not accounted for by the theory of humourism. The treatment's effects could be reproduced on multiple patients with similar afflictions; leading to the idea that different diseases could be classified, and that disease was not a patient-unique imbalance of humours.

French Medicine

Subsequently, in the Napoleonic and post-Napoleonic period, medicine saw a renovation forerun by French medicine. These reformations would include the integration of medicine and surgery to make practitioners better suited to the battlefields; development of the clinical examination with useful inventions such as the stethoscope, and an increased utilisation of pathology for diagnosis. At this stage, hospital care also rose to prominence.

Pioneers of Public Health

During the 18th century and beyond a new field of medicine was emerging called public health. Public health is concerned with protecting, and preserving the health of a nation as a whole, as opposed to treating ill individuals. Public health enthusiasts took an interest in epidemics (outbreaks of diseases e.g. Typhus); endemics (disease that is consistently maintained in an area, such as smallpox) and pandemics (large outbreaks of diseases encompassing the globe - for example, Plague, or Cholera (soon to emerge in the 19th Century). At the forefront of this new movement were two men called James Jurin and Edward Jenner, who would contribute to the progression of two public health initiatives: variolation (or inoculation) and vaccination, respectively.

James Jurin

During the 18th century, Small Pox was a cause of severe mortality across Europe (another pandemic). Smallpox had a relatively high mortality rate however it affected some people worse than others. People began to notice that once you had recovered from smallpox you seemed to have lifetime protection from it. Lady Mary Wortley Montagu postulated that if you infected a person with smallpox material from a less severe sufferer, then they were more likely to survive than if infected naturally. This process of administering material from one patient's smallpox pustules to another healthy individual was called variolation or inoculation. James Jurin (1684 – 1750 AD) was a physician who collected and published data on individuals undergoing smallpox variolation. He used statistics to show that variolation actually did reduce mortality. Jurin's work was vital in swaying the public opinion on inoculation – obviously nobody wanted to be given a potentially fatal condition unnecessarily, and this was a sticking point until another scientist continued the work.

Edward Jenner

Following on from the work of Jurin, was a physician named Edward Jenner (1749 – 1823 AD). Jenner observed that milkmaids often acquired a disease similar in presentation to Smallpox, but much less severe. None of these milkmaids seemed to get smallpox either. Jenner hypothesised that this 'Cowpox' conveyed immunity to Smallpox, and undertook an experiment to test this hypothesis. He injected some material from a Cowpox lesion (from a milkmaid), into the arm of a boy who had not been exposed to either disease – later the boy presented with the signs of Cowpox. After a six-week period, Jenner administered Smallpox material to the boy, but the boy did not develop the disease - indicating immunity. This vaccination (from the Latin for cow) using Cowpox material, could therefore prevent people from getting smallpox.

Miasmic or Contagion?

Throughout the 19th century there was an enduring battle between two factions, on the mechanism of disease transmission. These two groups were the Miasmatists and the contagionists, who each supported their own theory. In short, the miasmic theory dictated that disease was spread through the air (reflecting Hippocrates' work – on airs, waters and places), and it associated disease with malodourous substances such as human excrement. Supporters of this theory reasoned that this explained how diseases could affect people across whole continents so quickly. Conversely, the contagion theory suggested that disease was spread person-to-person; this could explain why individuals caring for the ill may themselves develop the disease. Contagiousness had been shown in smallpox inoculation studies, so contagionists theorised that this could be generalised to other diseases.

Edwin Chadwick

Edwin Chadwick (1800 – 1890 AD) was an English social reformer and the secretary of the Poor Law Commission. He was also a strong believer of the miasmic theory of disease. He theorised that disease was a causative factor of poverty and that if one reduced the prevalence of disease, poverty would soon follow suit. To do this Chadwick would have to develop the public health system of the country. As a Miasmist he thought foul, odorous objects and unsanitary conditions caused disease. He took inspiration from the Ancient Roman systems of aqueducts and sewerage, suggesting the implementation of separate sewerage and drinking water systems. Chadwick faced a lot of opposition in his time such as by, Thomas Robert Malthus, who indicated in his publication, *an essay on the principle of population*, that lower life expectancies in the poor, due to illness and starvation was nature's means to maintain the population at a sustainable level. Chadwick also wanted the public health scheme implemented in his own vision with little room for negotiation, and this ultimately led to his downfall.

John Snow

John Snow (1813 – 1858 AD) is one of the most renowned figures in medicine; contributing to both anaesthesiology and to the foundation of epidemiology – the study of the health and disease of populations. Snow invalidated the prevailing miasmic theory by undertaking a series of experiments, which demonstrated that cholera was transmitted through infected drinking water. In his most famous study he observed that all cholera sufferers in an area of London collected their drinking water from the same source – the broad street pump. Snow theorised that if they stopped collecting water from this source there would be a fall in the incidence of cholera – so he removed the pump handle! This resulted in fewer outbreaks.

Moghuls of Microbiology

During the latter part of the 19th century a new field would emerge – microbiology. This field was founded by three main figures: Pasteur, Koch and Cohn. Cohn is renowned for establishing a classification system of bacteria (dependant on their shape) that is still used today, and the discovery of endospores, or simply spores, – heat-resistant dormant bacteria. Pasteur and Koch, from France and Germany respectively, had a strong disdain for one another, which was understandable as they rose to prominence in the wake of the Franco-Prussian war between their two nations.

Louis Pasteur

Pasteur (1822 – 1895 AD) is renowned for experiments using his 'swan-neck flasks'. In these experiments Pasteur would boil a broth of nutrients in two beakers (one with a straight neck and one with a 'swan) to sterilise them. The flasks would then be allowed to cool. Bacteria would grow in the straight-necked broth but not the swan-necked broth, as they would pool in the curve of the neck. This disproved a prevailing theory that some organisms spontaneously came into being (spontaneous generation), and showed that they only grew in a broth that had been contaminated.

He made several other discoveries prior to his advocacy of germ theory (discussed next). He discovered that yeast-fermentation processes were biological and not chemical like many had thought. He also invented a process known as 'pasteurisation', which sterilised milk, in order to prolong its longevity. Pasteur was asked to study a disease of silk worms and treat it. He came to the conclusion that microorganisms were the pathogen, or the cause of the disease. This is in line with the germ theory of disease. Germ theory would supplant theories such as miasmic theory and shine light on why certain water supplies infected people with cholera whereas other water supplies did not – an enigma that had bested Snow.

Famously, Pasteur isolated *Anthrax bacilli* from a blood smear and attenuated it (made it weaker), converting it into a vaccine that prevented people from contracting anthrax. He also made a vaccine for rabies. This is particularly impressive as rabies is viral, and there was limited knowledge on virology at that time (scientists could not see viruses under their microscopes).

Elizabeth Blackwell

Blackwell (1821- 1920AD) was the first woman to be awarded a medical degree from the United States and was also the first woman to gain entry onto the UK medical register. Her motivation to become a doctor was in part a result of her friend's dying wish, to have been treated by a female doctor, as she felt that a woman would have been able to empathise with (and potentially ease) her suffering. This need to connect with patients as individuals, translates to the modern practices holistic and patient-centred medicine; treat the patient as a whole, maintaining treatment that is in their best interest and also treating them with respect and dignity. Practising holistic and patient-centred care are arguably as important today as all of the combined medical, surgical and scientific discoveries in history. At the end of the day, we are all people and the enduring factor that connects patients and their doctors, is our shared humanity.

Robert Koch

Across the border in Germany, Robert Koch (1843 – 1910 AD) was making his own discoveries in the field of microbiology. Koch used agar cultures (and later petri dishes thanks to his assistant Julius Petri), to grow bacteria, which were less prone to contamination than Pasteur's 'culture soups'. Like Pasteur he also studied anthrax and he determined the bacteria's lifecycle. Importantly, Koch travelled to India in an attempt to isolate the microbe responsible for cholera. After analysing the water supply and excrement of cholera patients, he identified a common organism – *Vibrio cholera.*

The scientific community were beginning to accept that germs might have some involvement in disease development (although many still disputed this). What remained a mystery was to what extent they contributed to disease. Some believed they were merely one of a plethora of causative factors whilst others felt they might be the sole determinant of certain diseases. Some standardised, testable criteria were needed to unravel this perplexity; there was a need to establish a causative relationship between microorganisms and disease – cue Koch's postulates (fig. 2). Koch used his postulates to confirm the bacteria responsible for Cholera as well as discovering the bacteria responsible for Tuberculosis (TB) – *Mycobacterium tuberculosis.* The latter was a tremendous achievement as TB is a fastidious bacterium (it is difficult to grow in culture and cannot be gram-stained).

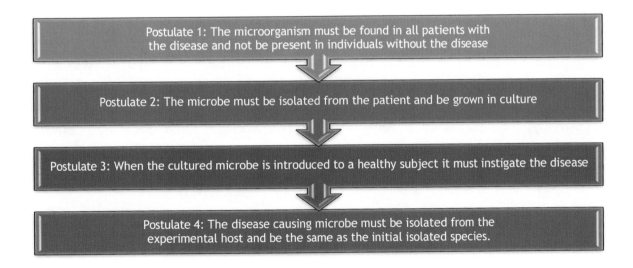

Figure 2: Koch's Postulates

Koch's postulates formulated the criteria for identifying pathogenic causes of disease.

In general Koch's postulates seemed to work (and still hold true today), however there are some exceptions. Koch later discovered the 'carrier state'. This is where individuals have the microorganism but do not present with the disease; contradicting Koch's first and third postulates. Furthermore, Not all microorganisms can be grown in culture and some are very difficult to culture (e.g. TB, as mentioned above), which contradicted his second postulate. Nowadays, the practical application of all four postulates on humans has somewhat diminished it is highly immoral (and probably illegal) to intentionally infect a human for the purposes of scientific study.

Modern Applications of Koch's Postulates

In the late 20th century the postulates were famously once again put to the test. Two doctors; **Robin Warren** and **Barry Marshall**, biopsied stomach ulcers to determine whether they had a pathogenic aetiology. In their experiments they successfully isolated the bacterium, *Helicobacter pylori.* They also found that this bacterium was present in stomach cancer biopsies. Stomach ulcers were a longstanding problem and the doctors believed they could be treated with antibiotics. At the time the scientific community were not convinced with the proposed aetiology and believed stomach ulcers were due to stress and other lifestyle factors. It seemed unlikely that bacteria could survive in the stomach, which for so long was considered a sterile site, due to its low pH. In the end Marshall decided to drink an H. Pylori broth (Koch's 3rd postulate) to prove that they were correct. He became very ill developing gastritis (inflammation of the stomach), which would ultimately lead to ulceration. His stomach was biopsied and H. pylori was isolated (Koch's 4th postulate). He then successfully treated his gastritis with antibiotics. Subsequently, they published a paper in 1984 and won the noble prize for medicine in 2005.

Advocates of Anaesthesia and Antisepsis

The 19th century developments in anaesthesia would improve tolerability to surgery, allowing for more severe interventions, whilst advances in antisepsis would minimise deaths due to infection. The use of anaesthesia has a long history supposedly dating back to the 2nd century AD when Chinese surgeon **Hua Tuo** used an anaesthetic derived from hemp, during his operations. During the middle ages there had been some mild success with the use of opiates and later an opiate-based concoction known as Dwale. During the 18th century, Sir Humphrey Davis discovered the anaesthetic properties of Nitrous Oxide, later to be coined as 'laughing gas'. It wasn't until the 19th century however, that effective surgical anaesthesia (elimination of sensation), seemed to have been obtained. This was initiated by the Americans with their use of Ether in surgery; a substance that would later prove unsuitable for theatre due to its extreme volatility. The Scottish physician **James Simpson** (1811 – 1870 AD) would provide an alternative to ether when he discovered the anaesthetic properties of chloroform. This drug would be approved later, when John Snow used it on Queen Victoria to ease her childbirth. Chloroform, however, also had its problems. Many individuals who inhaled the substance would never regain consciousness from anaesthesia – people started to die. Snow studied this and realised that too much chloroform resulted in the heart stopping. He then invented a chloroform inhaler and a dosage system to address this problem.

Ignaz Semmelweis

Germ theory contributed to the field of surgery, as surgeons sought to develop antiseptics (substances that would eliminate pathogens in wounds). However, the field of antiseptics was formed prior to germ theory, unwittingly, by a Hungarian physician named Ignaz Semmelweis (1818 – 1865 AD). Semmelweis noticed that women on doctors-led wards had a higher mortality from puerperal fever (a post-pregnancy illness), than on midwife-led wards. The only significant difference between doctors' and midwives' deliveries was that doctors often visited the mortuary beforehand. Shortly after this observation, his friend and colleague Jakob Kolletschka would cut his finger during an autopsy. Kolletschka then developed the symptoms of puerperal fever and died. Semmelweis deduced that cadaveric contamination was the cause of puerperal fever. He proposed that if physicians washed their hands after dissecting bodies then the maternal mortality rate would fall. Semmelweis implemented a hand-washing scheme using chlorinated lime solution (antiseptic) prior to delivering babies, which greatly reduced puerperal fever and mortality. Semmelweis's research was criticised, because he could not provide any mechanism of action for dirty hands causing disease; his findings were prior to Pasteur's work on germ theory. His views of washing hands went against the medical establishment and were considered unnecessary. Henceforth, Semmelweis received constant criticism putting his resilience to the test. Eventually, he was sent to an asylum, where he rather ironically died from septicaemia.

Joseph Lister

It wasn't until the time of Pasteur that Semmelweis's ideas on hand hygiene and antisepsis would become accepted. From this point on, Joseph Lister (1827 – 1912 AD) would lead the development of antiseptics. He was aware that for many years carbolic acid was used to disinfect sewage and hypothesised that this could be applied to killing bacteria in wounds. He soaked bandages in carbolic acid and wrapped them around compound bone fractures (where the bone perforates the skin). This made the process of amputation for compound fractures almost obsolete, and improved surgical survival rates greatly. Antiseptics were soon replaced by aseptic techniques, which aimed to prevent pathogens entering wounds in the first place. This would involve sterilisation of surgical instruments, the surgeon's hands and the patient's skin.

The interesting case of Dr. James Miranda Steuart Barry (1795-1865)

James Barry went to great lengths to study medicine and practice as a surgeon. It was only discovered after his death that he was in fact a woman. As well as being a surgeon in the army, Dr. Barry used his knowledge of sanitation to improve the areas he was posted to. A key surgical achievement was one of the first successful caesarean sections, in which both the mother and baby survived.

20th Century Healthcare

During the 20th century there was a plethora of medical advances ranging from the basic sciences to clinical practice – far too many to mention here. Instead this next section is divided into three main areas: medicine, surgery and public health. This section will review a selection of accomplishments and advances in these three fields, during the 20th century.

1. Medicine

In 1921, **Frederick Banting** (a physiologist), **Charles Best** (a medical student) and **Bertrand Collip** (a biochemist), successfully isolated the molecule insulin from pancreatic samples. After administering this substance into the bloodstream of subjects, the team noticed that it reduced these individuals' blood sugar concentrations. This had enormous clinical implications, as up until this point there was no treatment for insulin-dependent (Type 1) diabetes. Insulin was successfully used to resuscitate individuals who had been in diabetic comas for years. This was the dawn of a whole new treatment era.

Alexander Fleming was a biologist who, in 1928, discovered a mold growing on one of his petri dishes – later to be called penicillin. Penicillin was the first mass produced antibiotic and is part of the β-lactam family. Antibiotics are substances naturally produced by microorganisms that kill or inhibit the growth of bacteria. Antibiotics could treat septic wounds; a major killer during the first and second world wars. Unfortunately, Fleming did not realise the potential benefits of this mold upon discovery, and it remained unused for years. It was not until World War II, that a team led by the Oxfordian pathologist, **Howard Florey**, tested penicillin and found it to be effective in curing infections. They then went about mass-producing the product, initially for wartime injuries and later for general infections. Penicillin and the subsequent antibiotics that arose following its discovery, seemed to be 'cure-alls' or 'magic bullets' (a phrase coined by Paul Ehrlich), which successfully treated a myriad of diseases. These antibiotic wonder drugs would gradually loose this reputation when doctors started noticing signs of antibiotic resistance (discussed further in the following chapter).

After the discovery of antibiotics came the discovery of antivirals. This began in the 1950s and by the 1960s the first anti-viral drug, idoxuridine, was in clinical use. This was used to treat herpetic keratitis, an eye infection caused by the herpes simplex virus. This has been largely replaced by aciclovir, an antiviral that is also effective against other herpetic pathogens such as varicella zoster virus – the cause of chickenpox in children and shingles in adults. The development of antiretroviral therapy (drugs that target retroviruses), has been one the greatest achievements in 20th century medicine. Retroviruses are RNA-based viruses that used the enzyme reverse transcriptase to code for viral DNA, which is integrated into the host DNA using DNA integrase. The host cell then reproduces the virus. The first antiretroviral approved for the treatment of Human Immunodeficiency Virus (HIV) was Zidovudine, a drug originally used for cancer treatment. Zidovudine is effective in slowing the progression of HIV but it is not a cure. Zidovudine is a nucleoside reverse transcriptase inhibitor, meaning that it competitively inhibits the reverse transcriptase enzyme. Nowadays, it is used in combination with different types of antiretrovirals – this is called highly active antiretroviral therapy (HAART).

In addition to antibiotics and antivirals, there was a requirement for immunosuppressant therapy for transplantation. Transplantation was unsuccessful due the body's rejection of the transplanted organ. Doctors first experimented with x-ray irradiation, which destroyed the immune cells. Patients were given bone marrow transplants to regain a level of immunity however most patients died from infections. Next came the idea of drug-induced immunosuppression where doctors experimented with Zidovudine. It had some successes in animal models but was not that effective in human transplantation. Serendipity struck when the Swiss pharmaceutical company Sandoz (now Novartis), sent an employee to collect soil samples from Norway in an attempt to discover new antibiotics. A fungal-product was isolated from the soil that had no antibiotic effect but seemed to lower the immune system. This substance, called Ciclosporin, soon became highly successful in preventing rejection of transplantation or tissue grafts.

Another advancement that would improve survival rates from trauma would be effective blood transfusions. This was initiated by **Karl Landsteiner**'s discovery of the ABO blood grouping system. In this system all humans have one type of red blood cell: A; B; AB or O. A-types have A-markers on their red blood cells, B-types have B-markers, AB-type have both markers and O-type have neither. If doctors transfuse the wrong type of blood into a patient's circulatory system, it could lead to haemolytic anaemia. This is a process where the recipient's immune system destroys the transfused red blood cells, recognising the surface markers as 'non-self'; potentially leading to anaphylaxis and death. The efficiency of transfusions was furthered by the inclusion of sodium citrate, which prevented the clotting of blood. By the 1930s, blood could be separated into its constituent parts (e.g. red blood cells, platelets, plasma) and the type of transfusion depended on what was required. The rhesus blood grouping system would also be discovered in the 20th century. Human red blood cells are either rhesus positive or rhesus negative. This system is independent of the ABO system, explaining why some blood transfusions may lead to haemolytic anaemia in ABO-matched recipients.

Marie Curie (1897- 1934) was a Polish Physicist and Chemist who became a pioneer in the field of radiation research. She was the first women to be awarded a Nobel Prize in Physics in 1903, and was later awarded a 2nd Nobel Prize in Chemistry in 1911. Working with her husband, Pierre Curie, she discovered Polonium and Radium. Marie Curie made a significant contribution to medicine also, because she supervised the use of radioactive isotopes to treat tumours, and developed a portable radiography machine to be used during World War I. These machines became well known as 'Little Curies', and by the end of the war over a million soldiers had been examined.

Imaging was a medical development that had surgical implications. It allowed radiologists to identify where the problem was; what the problem was and the best way for the surgeon to tackle the problem. This started at the end of the 19th century when **Wilhelm Roentgen** discovered X-rays. These became very popular in the 1940s, not only on the battlefields but also back at home where portable x-ray vans would be used to screen whole nations for disease. It was later found that high-dosage radiation led to people developing leukaemia and other types of cancers, and tighter regulations were placed on x-ray screening. Interestingly, this phenomenon can still be seen today in individuals undergoing radiotherapy for cancer, which itself can induce cancer. Subsequently, computerised topography (CT) would be developed that uses multiple x- ray scans to produce a cross-sectional image (a slice through the body). Ultrasound machines came into use for pregnancy screens amongst other things. These use high-frequency sound bouncing off objects to produce an image. By the 1970s, magnetic resonance imaging or MRI scans were available, which use a magnetic field to produce images. These are particularly useful, as they show soft tissue in greater detail than CT – although CT scanners keep improving.

A scoring system was devised (and named after) **Virginia Apgar** (1909- 1974), in 1952.

Apgar was an American obstetric anaesthesiologist whose 'APGAR Score', allowed doctors to quickly assess the health of a neonate shortly after birth. The score is calculated by assessing five domains with a maximum of two points per domain. APGAR is an ackronym for the five domains: **A**ppearance, **P**ulse, **G**rimace, **A**ctivity & **R**espiration. The benefit of using this scoring system is that it allows doctors to assess whether the neonate needs additional support after birth, ultimately reducing any complications that may arise.

Even by the 20th century, psychiatry was a still relatively young field, having been formed by **Philippe Pinel** in the 19th century. At this time, 'lunatics' were admitted to madhouses, then later asylums; these were essentially the same as madhouses but on a larger scale. In the 1940s, physician **Walter Freeman** and neurosurgeon **James Watts** would attempt to resolve these seemingly untreatable conditions through operations known as lobotomies and leukotomies. These operations aimed to sever the connections between the front parts of brain in an attempt to treat psychiatric disorders, by making the patient's more docile. Freeman believed that he perfected this process with his invention of the trans-orbital lobotomy, which basically involved hammering an ice pick through the back of the orbit (eye socket), shattering bone and destroying brain tissue. These procedures were controversial and caused many complications, such as permanent brain damage (beyond what was intended) and even death. For example, a 12-year-old boy called **Howard Dully** received a trans-orbital lobotomy simply because his stepmother thought it would fix his bad behaviour. Instead of amending his behaviour it caused him to become more erratic, an alcoholic and ultimately (and ironically) he was institutionalised. It took him many years to regain control of his life and he eventually managed to get a job as a bus driver.

Fortunately, the latter half of the 20th century saw real progression in psychiatric care, with psychotropic medication becoming available in the 1950s. These medications were the first successful methods for treating mental conditions, such as depression, anxiety and psychosis. Many institutionalised patients who were previously considered insane became outpatients with normal lives. This led to community psychiatry, where patients could be cared for and treated at home. This was aided by the development of (psychological) behavioural therapies from learning theory, in the 1960s. One example is response prevention, which is still used to treat Obsessive Compulsive Disorder (OCD). Mental illness stigma and problems with dehumanisation in psychiatric institutes, were further addressed in the 1970s via the publication of psychologist **David Rosenhan's** experiment, 'on being sane in insane places'. Towards the end of the century, surgery would regain prominence in the field of mental health and neurology, with the invention of deep brain stimulation (DBS), which involves implanting an electrode in a specific area of the brain. DBS addresses the symptoms of many diseases. In 1997 DBS was approved for essential tremor and later in the 21st century for other diseases such as Parkinson's disease and OCD.

2. Surgery

In the 20th century two cousins, **Harold Gilles** and **Archibald McIndoe**, would pioneer modern plastic surgery. Gilles started the transformation during the First World War. He synthesised all the knowledge of French wartime surgery and used experimentation to tend to soldiers who had their faces mutilated by shrapnel. He revived and renovated the forehead flap employed by Sushruta, by placing rib cartilage under the skin of the forehead first, as this gave a better nasal structure than Sushruta's original method. The next hurdle for Gilles to overcome was the fact that many of his patients were dying from infection due to exposed flesh. He adopted and modified a Russian idea to get around this problem, creating the tube pedicle. This involved wrapping the skin up into a tube to prevent entry of pathogens. The pedicle was initially connected from the leg to the arm, then later detached from the leg and connected from the arm to the face. In his later years, Gilles would use the tube pedicle to successfully create an artificial penis in the first female to male sex change.

McIndoe, inspired by the work of his cousin, carried on the development of plastic surgery through the Second World War and established a hospital to treat burnt airmen. He formed the 'guinea pig club' of patients, which reflects just how experimental his work was. An important advancement was an appreciation of mental illness in rehabilitation. He recognised that many of his patients had psychological trauma associated with disfigurements, making it difficult for them to adjust. He put the servicemen in the public eye, and asked people to not treat them differently so that they could be reintegrated into society. This was a huge progression from Gilles' patients, who felt isolated due to their perceived disfigurements and often committed suicide.

By the 1970s, surgeons developed a technique that bypassed the use of pedicles – microsurgery. Microsurgery involves free tissue transfer or reattaching severed limbs through the formation of anastomosis (connections) between arteries, veins and nerves of the donor tissue and recipient site. This process requires an operating microscope, as the vessels are usually around 1mm in diameter.

Entering the 21st century, plastic surgery has advanced to a stage where we can offer full-face transplants. In December 2012, a team led by **Professor Simon Kay**, a Consultant plastic surgeon in Leeds General Infirmary, performed the first UK hand transplant. Although the surgical techniques have progressed to this stage, the longevity of these transplants equally depends on the patient's treatment of them. In 1998, **Clint Hallam** was the world's first recipient of a hand transplant. He struggled to adapt to his transplant and did not consider it to be his own hand. He also found the side effects of his immunotherapy unbearable and cut down his dosage, which ultimately, led to his immune system rejecting his hand. He later had it removed. He now uses a prosthetic hand which he feels that he is more comfortable with.

The heart was something that just was not surgically treatable until the 20th century; prio to this, death nearly always followed any surgical intervention. This would be changed during the Second World War by a U.S. surgeon called **Dwight Harken,** who designed a method to cut into the heart and pull out shrapnel with his finger. Suddenly, surgeons all over the world decided to dabble with cardiac surgery themselves – many attempting to fix congenital (defects from birth) problems, such as holes in the heart. One major problem with this was that heart surgery required the aorta and vena cava to be clamped to prevent excessive bleeding. However, more than four minutes of clamping would result in permanent brain damage due to lack of oxygen. For complex congenital problems, four minutes was not long enough. A Canadian surgeon called **William Bigelow** found the answer to this. He theorised that if he slowed the body's metabolic rate he could extend the window before brain damage occurred. Bigelow achieved this in several canine experiments by inducing hypothermia, but also by administering ether to prevent them shivering, which would otherwise increase oxygen consumption. Two American surgeons called **John Lewis** and **Walt Lillehei**, used Bigelow's findings to successfully perform cardiac surgery on a young girl called Jacqueline Johnson, who had a congenital heart defect. Eventually, refined techniques of hypothermia would allow up to 10 minutes of vessel clamping before any brain damage occurred.

In an attempt to widen the operating window, Lillehei developed a 'cross-circulation' method instead of inducing hypothermia. This involved connecting the patients venous system to a healthy donor's femoral (thigh) vein where it would be oxygenated in the donor's body and reconnected to the patient's carotid artery to maintain a body supply to the patient's brain. In essence, this system used a healthy volunteer to oxygenate and circulate blood around two bodies. Lillehei had some great successes with this procedure performing otherwise inoperable surgery. Cross-circulation had the potential to harm healthy donors and was later scrapped when a healthy donor developed permanent brain damage. This was an important development as Lillehei's method broke the ethical principle of non-maleficence or doing no harm (see chapter on medical ethics).

John Gibbon was a physician, who spent many years working on a device that could bypass the heart and lungs; oxygenating blood in a machine which would then deliver this oxygenated blood back to the body. In years to come this type of machine would 'stop the clock', that cardiac surgeons so far had to adhere to. Unfortunately, this would not occur in Gibbons time and several of his patients would die in surgery whilst using his machine. He later retired from cardiac surgery and ironically died of heart disease. Others would later refine Gibbon's machine and surgeons would utilise potassium chloride injections to stop the heart beating, making surgery easier. Cardiac surgery progressed with **Christian Barnard,** a South African surgeon who would perform the first heart transplant in 1967.

Paradoxically, after all of the hard work of making heart surgery successful, the specialty is now shrinking and becoming replaced by less invasive laparoscopic procedures. Laparoscopy is often referred to as minimally invasive or keyhole surgery. It involves performing surgery through small incisions in the skin where surgeons insert a long thin camera (laparoscope), and surgical instruments. This method ultimately leads to less scarring, shorter recovery periods and less risk of infections. Vascular surgeons (and interventional radiologists) are now taking over from cardiac surgeons, with procedures such as coronary angiography (stenting) being preferable to open-heart surgery procedures (such as coronary artery bypasses). Some have speculated that cardiovascular surgery may soon completely vanish as a specialty.

3. Public Health

Arguably the greatest achievement in 20th century public health was the establishment of a National Health Service or NHS in 1948, by health minister **Aneurin Bevin**. The NHS was established to provide healthcare that was free at the point of delivery. This means that you do not have to pay for services when you use the NHS but you pay for the system through national taxation. This model was not economically sustainable and in 1952 prescription and dental charges were introduced.

Initially, the British Medical Association, the trade union for doctors, was strongly opposed to the NHS, but over time this position changed and they are now advocates for the service. The NHS has greatly improved the health of the nation and provides healthcare to those who could not previously afford it and relied upon philanthropic hospitals.

Shortly after the establishment of the NHS (1951), a doctor called **Richard Doll** published a paper in the British Medical Journal on the relationship between cigarette smoking and lung cancer. There had been a significant increase in the number of lung cancer related deaths after the First World War and doll conducted an epidemiological study to identify the cause. Expecting industrial fumes or tarmac to be the cause of this disease, he was surprised to find that people who smoked were at an increased risk of developing lung cancer. Nowadays, deaths from smoking are still high but would have been considerably higher without the findings of his study and consequent public health initiatives (e.g. stop smoking campaigns).

The 20th century saw great achievements in vaccination campaigns. In 1952 **Jonas Salk** developed a vaccine that would prevent the development of Poliomyelitis (Polio) – a disease that can affect the muscles of the limbs. Although Salk developed an effective vaccine it was not popular and was instead replaced by a vaccine produced by **Alfred Sabin**. Sabin's vaccine was taken orally by adding it to a lump of sugar, which made it appealing to children. It is important to realise that although a vaccine or treatment may be effective, people may not opt for it if the administration or side effects are unpleasant. Today worldwide eradication of Polio has almost been reached. In 1980, the World Health Organisation officially declared Smallpox eradiated due to the combined implementation of effective vaccination programmes worldwide. The last natural case of small pox occurred in Somalia in 1977 but the following year a medical photographer at Birmingham Medical School accidently contracted the disease and sadly died. From 1971 onwards the Measles, Mumps and Rubella (MMR) combination vaccine was released to tackle the incidence of these three childhood diseases. In general this vaccine has had good uptake, however there was a drop in the uptake at the start of the 21st century following the MMR scandal.

Industrial pollution was a particular problem in the early 20th century, affecting both individual health and the environment. In 1952 the 'great smog' swept over London affecting visibility. The event led to somewhere between 4000-12,000 deaths and caused respiratory tract illness in over 100,000, although the event was thought to be insignificant at the time. In 1956, the Clean Air Act was passed which reduced air pollution through conversion of home energy supplies from coal to electricity, and smokeless fuels such as gas. The amount of sulphur dioxide in fuel was reduced and power stations were moved away from cities.

In 1980 the ever-growing health inequalities in Britain would be dragged into the limelight through the publication of the Black Report. The document was written by **Sir Douglas Black** and published by what is now the Department of Health. It showed that although health in general had improved since the introduction of the 'welfare state' (government policies to improve national health, education, employment and social status), inequalities in health between the highest and lowest social classes have actually increased. This report would be followed by 'Fair Society Healthy Lives, The Marmot Review' in 2010 by **Professor Sir Michael Marmot,** who identified six policies to reduce health inequalities:

1. Give every child the best start in life.

2. Enable all children, young people and adults to maximise their capabilities and have control over their lives.

3. Create fair employment and good work for all.

4. Ensure healthy standards of living for all.

5. Create and develop healthy and sustainable places and communities.

6. Strengthen the role and impact of ill-health prevention.

Although there were many great achievements in 20th century public health policy, the outlook was not all positive. At the turn of the century the eugenics movement started to gain traction. Eugenics is concerned with improving the human genetic stock, through positive methods of selecting desirable traits in people (similar to selective breeding in animals), and negative methods such as sterilisation (amongst those with less desirable traits). Eugenics is often associated with the Nazis, who did indeed instigate eugenic programmes, however it is important to note that however unethical the concept is today, the movement had much global support at the time. Many figures from the UK supported eugenics including Winston Churchill, but no schemes were nationally implemented. The Unites States, on the other hand, began implementing eugenics programmes even prior to the Nazis. You may wish to return to the ever controversial subject of Eugenics, when you cover medical ethics in Chapter 3.

 # Chapter 2: Contemporary Healthcare Issues

Mentor's Tip

In this chapter the Mentors will critically review an array of threats assailing 21st century healthcare. A sound knowledge of fundamental issues such as A&E and outpatient waiting times, and chronic understaffing in general practice, shows interviewers that you have an insight into the everyday workings of the NHS. This in turn gives them the impression that you are motivated to pursue a career in medicine and that you know what type of career to are getting into. This chapter is highly interactive: you will be asked to consider thought-provoking questions and ethical dilemmas, to help you develop a deeper understanding of conceptually difficult topics. Interview style questions regarding these areas are covered in **Medic Mentor's Interview Skills Checklist**, *which works in conjunction with the knowledge disseminated here.*

Old Persisting Problems

During the twentieth century the world succumbed to a variety of tragic diseases. HIV/AIDS was on the rise and the number of deaths attributed to cancer was ever increasing. Although these conditions are still prevalent today they are progressively being tackled. HIV patients can now live a near normal life on HAART. Cancer is being addressed through preventative public health campaigns; for example, advising the use of sun lotion on holidays and the provision of smoking cessation services. The effects of these campaigns are augmented by the development of new medical, surgical and imaging techniques. Recently, research has been published on two new fluorescent markers called CLR1501 and CLR1502. These markers have been shown to stain tumour tissue differently to normal brain tissue. This has the potential to make surgical excision of cancer easier. It also minimises human error, as the surgeon is less likely to miss parts of the tumour.

HIV used to be highly stigmatised and it still is to some degree. When it first broke out, the disease was referred to as gay-related immunodeficiency (GRID); public health scientists noticed rare opportunistic diseases in homosexual populations, that required the patient to have a lowered immune system (this is essential a clinical description of AIDS). The proposed homosexual aetiology (cause of disease), just reflects how little we knew about it. Today, the medical profession is actively combatting HIV-related stigma. In 2013, the government ruled that HIV-positive surgeons should be allowed to perform operations again, after an initial ban. This movement has been supported by the BMA. There are several conditions that have to be met to ensure patient safety. These are that patients must be on HAART and their viral load (a measure of the amount of a virus in the bloodstream) must be undetectable. Additionally, public health staff will monitor the surgeon's viral load and treatment adherence to ensure safeguarding of patients.

Ethical Dilemma: *Do you think surgeons with HIV should be allowed to perform surgery? Does it unnecessarily put the patients at risk? Is it unfair to make a surgeon retire from their profession because they contract a communicable disease?*

Write your answer here:

Two other age-old diseases still enduring are: Tuberculosis (TB) and Malaria. Both of these conditions are highly infectious. The bacteria *Mycobacterium tuberculosis* causes TB. Malaria is caused by parasitic protozoans (a type of unicellular eukaryote) of the genus *Plasmodium,* and is transmitted by the female anopheles mosquito vector. There are various reasons why these infections as still so prevalent. The infecting species of both diseases show multi-drug resistance, which means that new treatments must be continually devised because the pathogens develop drug resistance. Tuberculosis can be asymptomatic in healthy people and symptoms only present when that person is immunocompromised, therefore it can spread unnoticed. Malaria has a disease reservoir of anopheles mosquitos and it is not possible to exterminate all of these. Until very recently we have had no vaccine for malaria. In April 2015 a paper was published in the Lancet concerning RTS,S/AS01 – a malaria vaccine candidate. This vaccine has been shown to work in final stage clinical trials and is the only candidate to reach this stage so far. However, the vaccine only seems to be 46% effective, much lower than what researchers would hope for.

Ethical Dilemma: *Do you think people should be health-screened for infectious diseases before entering the UK?*

Write your answer here:

Ethical Dilemma: If screenings took place, should patients be treated on-site/at a nearby hospital, or sent back home for treatment?

Write your answer here:

Food for Thought: How do you decide which diseases are permissible for entry? On a scale from the common cold to Ebola, where would you mark the cut-off?

Write your answer here:

Zoonotic Troubles

In November 2002, severe acute respiratory syndrome commonly referred to as SARS broke out in China. SARS was a disease caused by *SARS Coronavirus,* that resulted in severe illness and almost 800 deaths. This epidemic was zoonotic in origin, meaning that the disease was spread from animals to humans. Another coronavirus epidemic called Middle East respiratory syndrome or MERS, struck in May 2015. MERS is also a zoonotic condition and camels are thought to have some involvement in the disease transmission.

Zoonosis is an important mechanism of disease transmission, in a world where connectivity and travel is ever increasing. There are various well-known conditions that spread from animals to humans such as rabies and foot-and-mouth disease. Probably the most prominent zoonotic disease of all time is influenza. In 2003 Robert Webster, a leading virologist published an article about influenza called, 'the world is teetering on the edge of a pandemic that could kill a large fraction of the human population'. This reflected his view that influenza was going to be the next 'big killer'. The following year in 2004, bird flu (or more correctly Avian Influenza) began to spread across the globe; leading to the deaths of millions of birds. Bird flu is caused by the influenza A subtype H5N1. Mass culling regimes were utilised to prevent transmission to humans, however these were not entirely effective. In 2013, the World Health Organisation (WHO) announced that 375 people died from bird flu over the preceding ten years.

Food for thought: Which do you think is a better disease prevention method for zoonosis, immunisation of healthy livestock or culling of diseased livestock?

Write your answer here:

Five years after the emergence of bird flu, arose a new threat – the **swine flu pandemic**. Swine flu was caused by an **H1N1** subtype of influenza. This was the second time that an H1N1 pandemic had occurred. The first pandemic was the **Spanish flu of 1918**, which killed more people than the First World War. It infected around half a billion people with some reports estimating 100 million fatalities. During the swine flu pandemic a variety of vaccines were released to prevent initial infection such as **Pandemrix**, produced by pharmaceutical giant **GlaxoSmithKline** (**GSK**). It was later discovered that children and young people who received Pandemrix developed **narcolepsy,** six times more often than those who did not have the vaccine. This is important to note as although modern pharmaceutical research is heavily scrutinised, there is always a chance that the product may deliver undesirable results. Initial reports from the WHO indicated that around 18,500 died from pandemic swine flu, however, recent research published in the PLOS medical journal in 2013 indicates that the actual death toll might have been ten times this figure. This figure may have been even greater if vaccines such as Pandemrix were not made available and arguably, the development of narcolepsy in some subjects may have been the lesser of two evils.

Food for Thought: Considering influenza strains change year to year, do you think it is worth all citizens being vaccinated every year in terms of disease prevention?

Write your answer here:

Food for Thought: What about immunising just the immunocompromised?

Write your answer here:

Food for Thought: Is it cost-effective for the NHS to buy all vaccinations produced by the pharmaceutical industries?

Write your answer here:

Food for Thought: If we devised a suitable vaccine for Rhinovirus (the cause of the common cold) would it be worth administering? Consider the cost of the vaccine for the NHS, the severity of the disease and its incubation period. Read up on these!

Write your answer here:

It is apparent that zoonotic disease affects the world substantially and poses a significant challenge for public health campaigns to address. This is done through **'One Health'**. One Health is the philosophy that partnership between multiple professions working at local, national and global levels will enable us to optimise health for animals, humans and the environment. The 19th century physician **Rudolf Virchow** said, "between animal and human medicine there are no dividing lines – nor should there be". This is an underlying concept in the One Health movement. The **One Health Commission** is a collaborative organisation in America established to achieve the aims of One Health. Its workforce includes members of the American Medical Association and the American Veterinary Medical Association, amongst other organisations.

Food for Thought: Do you think these interdisciplinary schemes should be trickled down into undergraduate medical education? How would medical schools go about this process?

Write your answer here:

An appreciation of **interdisciplinary work** such as that carried out by the One Health Commission is imperative for any aspiring doctor. This is because doctors are required to work in **multidisciplinary teams (MDTs)** throughout their careers. MDTs are composed of a variety of different healthcare staff, each with different skillsets and expertise. Utilising the skills of multiple professions, helps to deliver the best patient care from point of admission to long-term rehabilitation. An MDT for a patient who has had a stroke could include:

- **A consultant neurologist** – the medical lead who will assess the patient's general neurological functioning during ward rounds.

- **Junior doctors (FY1/FY2)** – these doctors will generally spend more time on the ward than the consultant and can check up on patients between ward rounds.

- **Physiotherapist** – these healthcare professionals assist stroke patients with a variety of exercises to help patients regain movement and muscle function.

- **Speech & language therapist** – these therapists are important for helping patients regain their speech after a stroke.

- **Nurses** – the nurses spend most of their time on the ward and are involved in the general care of the patients. This includes (amongst man other roles) personal care, monitoring observations, liaising closely with other professionals and the management and prevention of bedsores from lack of movement.

- **Occupational therapist** – OTs are essential in patients' rehabilitation, as they assess whether the patients' work and living conditions are suitable for them to return to, once they leave hospital.

- **Social workers** – are usually involved after discharge and assess the patients' social situation, family support and safety in their home enviroment.

Food for Thought: Recalling your medical work experience can you think of which staff members made up the multidisciplinary team? How did they uniquely contribute to patients' care?

Write your answer here:

It is highly beneficial to attend an **MDT meeting** if you get the opportunity, this will give you good insight into how various healthcare professionals work together to deliver excellent care. Often in the hospital you will notice doctors leading the team, for example, when a consultant is leading their ward round. In MDT meetings different members of staff may take a leading role in the presentation of a patient's case, therefore attending a meeting will give you an appreciation of the diversity of leadership.

Ebola: the Fever that Spread Fear in Millions

On the 23rd March 2014, the first death from the ongoing Ebola crisis was reported. Ebola virus disease or simply Ebola, is a disease caused by various species of the *Ebola virus* genus. It presents first as a fever, sore throat and muscular ache; then later as diarrhoea and vomiting and finally internal and external bleeding. It has an extremely high mortality rate with approximately 50-90% of those infected dying. Ebola may appear to be a new disease, as until recently it was relatively unknown to many, however, there have been multiple Ebola outbreaks across Africa since its discovery in 1976.

The disease is spread to humans from its natural reservoir: bushmeat. Bushmeat is a general term for animals hunted for food, including bats and chimpanzees. It is believed that human contact with these animals' blood is the mechanism of disease transfer to humans. Ebola is a highly infectious disease and is spread amongst human populations through contact with bodily fluids. It can also be transmitted through cuts and wounds that come into contact with infected inanimate objects, referred to as fomites. The virus causes death by inducing extreme dehydration and multiple organ failure. Currently there is no cure for Ebola; patients are quarantined and given intravenous fluids to prevent dehydration. In advanced hospital settings, patients may receive ventilation and dialysis to support their organs.

The most recent epidemic killed five times as many people as all other previous outbreaks together, and had a mortality rate of around 70%. Over 11,000 people died with most deaths occurring in Liberia, Sierra Leone and Guinea, respectively. This recent strain of Ebola was traced back to the death of an infant in a small village in Guinea in December 2013. By June 2014 the charity Medecins Sans Frontieres declared that the epidemic was out of control.

During this crisis, multiple Western volunteers contracted Ebola and some even died. The UK and USA (amongst other places) flew back volunteers for treatment. It is worth noting that both nations took the upmost precautions in preventing disease transmission during transportation and treatment. The Centre of Disease Control (CDC) in America stated that the US has the resources to treat and contain Ebola from transported patients. However, there is mixed public opinion on whether transporting patients home is a wise decision.

> *Food for Thought: Can you think of any sociocultural issues that erect barriers to healthcare or reduce adherence to medication in the UK? How would you address these issues?*

Write your answer here:

Treatment of Ebola has been hindered by local people's scepticism of western medicine and practices. This highlights how **sociocultural differences** between native populations and foreign interventions can have negative implications on the provision of healthcare.

> ***Food for Thought***: *Can you think of any sociocultural issues that erect barriers to healthcare or reduce adherence to medication in the UK? How would you address these issues?*

Write your answer here:

Mentor'sTip

A study in Kenya found that many locals did not use the white mosquito nets they were provided with, because they associated them with burial shrewds and death. To increase uptake of the mosquito nets it would be advisable to produce the nets in different colours. The connotations associated with the white nets were only realised through effective communication, and a resolution can only be achieved through working in partnership with the local community. Ultimately, a measure as simple as changing the colour of a mosquito net could improve the health of a community.

Sociocultural beliefs have affected the disease management of the Ebola crisis and in turn the disease has had sociocultural consequences of its own. Handshaking and hugging are common practices, both culturally and religiously in the affected African countries. However, these practices have been actively discouraged due to the highly infective nature of Ebola. Many burial procedures in these countries require the dead to be washed, however this has also been prohibited for safety reasons.

Due to the severity of the Ebola crisis, the WHO has permitted early trials of vaccines and experimental treatments, which have not been tested as thoroughly as most medications on the market. This is an unprecedented move on their behalf and raises ethical concerns.

Ethical Dilemma: *Do you think it is acceptable to use experimental treatments considering how high the mortality rate is?*

Write your answer here:

Ethical Dilemma: *Do you think there is too much regulation on experimental drugs in general or is it important for safeguarding patients?*

Write your answer here:

Mentor's Tip

*In 2013 **Lord Saatchi**, a member of the House of Lords, called for the use of experimental drugs to treat medical conditions. This request was made after his own wife died from ovarian cancer. This medical innovations bill would allow experimental medicine to be used for any medical condition, without the doctor fearing litigation. The bill received a lot of support through the media and was openly endorsed by several doctors. However, over 100 medical professionals signed a document to The Times, indicating that the bill would undermine evidence-based medicine and lead to a regressive anecdotal-based system. An article in the Lancet Oncology warned that the bill would go against the Hippocratic oath.*

The Ebola treatment trials have caused a schism in global scientific opinion. Some scientists believe that the use of a control group is unethical whilst others believe that the exclusion of a control group is unethical. A control group is necessary to determine if a treatment truly works or not, by comparing the results with that of the study group. Although randomised double-blind trials (discussed further in the understanding research chapter on page 107) are the gold standard of research, the WHO trials chose to exclude control groups as the majority of patients who only receive therapies such as intravenous fluids die and withholding treatment would result in death. Furthermore, they believed that withholding a potentially life-saving treatment from some Ebola patients is unethical in nature and would further impinge on the trust between local communities and foreign voluntary workers. Many doctors and researchers in Europe take this stance. An Oxford research team has chosen to compare their treatment group outcomes with data on historical Ebola outcomes, rather than using control groups. In general, WHO-supported trials follow this methodology, however some trials in Guinea using 'convalescent serum' (a blood product taken from patients who have recovered from Ebola thought to convey some level of immunological protection) will include a control group if there is no blood type matched serum available for some of the subjects.

There is strong opposition in the United States to the exclusion of control groups. Firstly, it will prevent scientific evaluation of a drug's efficacy. This will be counterproductive, because in subsequent Ebola epidemics we will still not know which drugs work. Furthermore, the experimental drugs may have severe unknown side effects, which certain patients would not be exposed to if a control group existed. In this way, having a control group could actually prevent some patients from further harm. There is also disapproval of trials using historical controls rather than placebo controls as the mortality rate varies greatly between datasets. The National Institute of Health (NIH) in America is currently running the only trial with a control group who are receiving a placebo. They are trialling a drug call ZMapp, which successfully treated all subjects in the preliminary animal trial. ZMapp is a chimeric monoclonal antibody meaning that it is genetically engineered from the fusion of multiple antibodies parts from different species (In the case of ZMapp formation, the process includes, human, mice and tobacco plant material). The following quotes summarise the American stance well:

"The idea that there's no need for randomised, controlled trials presupposes that the drugs have zero side effects, that they are efficacious, and that there's no substantial variability from patient to patient," Clifford Lane, a deputy director at the US National Institute of Allergy and Infectious Diseases.

"We couldn't do this in the U.S., and you couldn't do it in the U.K., so why do you think you can do it in Africa?" Andre Kalil, University of Nebraska Ebola Doctor.

Food for Thought: Do you think this Atlantic division in drug trial methodology reflects the differences in UK and USA healthcare systems? (Read more in the chapter concerning NHS structure and policy).

Write your answer here:

The Ebola crisis seems to be winding down with Liberia, the country with the highest death toll, being declared Ebola free in early May. Some researchers have speculated that the virus will not vanish, but instead will become endemic to certain areas of Africa – only time will tell.

Lifestyle Disease Versus the 'Nanny State' – How Far do we go with Public Health?

During the 19th and 20th century, infectious diseases such as Smallpox and Polio were major threats to the Western world. In the 21st century, we now face a plethora of health problems encompassed by the terms lifestyle diseases or diseases of affluence. These diseases are chronic and non-communicable. The onset and progression of these diseases depend on diet, longevity and other lifestyle factors such as the amount of exercise an individual undertakes. A few examples of these types of diseases include: Obesity, Type 2 Diabetes and Chronic Obstructive Pulmonary Disease (COPD). Over the last century, our diets have changed to include more red meat, saturated fats, and sugars; associated with an increase in cancer. In the early 20th century, heart disease was the 8th largest killer in the United States and it is now the largest, reflecting our diet transformation.

The Department of Health and associated organisations have issued various health policies and strategies to tackle the ever-increasing problem of lifestyle diseases. The National Institute of Health and Care Excellence (NICE) promotes behaviour change interventions. These illustrate the benefits of changing from an unhealthy behaviour to a healthy one, and encourage people to make these changes. Examples of these changes in terms of cardiovascular disease would be cessation of smoking, engaging in physical activity, minimising alcohol intake and changing to a more balanced diet.

In terms of specific undertakings, NICE produced clinical guideline 43 on obesity, managers and healthcare. This requires NHS staff to speak to patients about healthy eating if they are at risk of cardiovascular disease. General practitioners should also periodically discuss weight, diet and exercise habits with clinically obese patients.

Patients who are not losing weight with these interventions should then be referred to specialist weight management services in attempt to induce behavioural changes. Similar policies exist for addressing the prevalence of smoking in the UK. The Local Government Association aim to reduce smoking, as illustrated in their health strategy *'Healthy Lives, Healthy People: A Tobacco Control Plan for England'*, through several methods such as reducing the promotion of cigarettes and providing smoking cessation services. Importantly, the association aim to make smoking less affordable - this is a restrictive policy.

Although measures to tackle determinants of lifestyle disease have been established with good intentions, some people consider the policies too invasive. Increasing implementation of restrictive policies and guidance on 'the healthier way' to live your life leads to the public perceiving the government as a Nanny State. A Nanny State is a pejorative term for an overprotective government, who unnecessarily interferes with people's personal liberties. Medical organisations that conduct their actions in this way are regarded as paternalistic.

Paternalism involves one party restricting the choices of another party for their perceived benefit. During the 20th century paternalism was ubiquitous in Medicine, with patients regarding the doctor's decision as final. Rapidly, this custom has (mostly) vanished from clinical practice and has been replaced by patient-centred care. Patient-centred care involves patients in the treatment decision-making process, and respects the patient's autonomy even if the doctor thinks their decision is unwise. Patient-centred care is now engrained into NHS practice and is stipulated in the GMC document, Tomorrow's *Doctors*. However the transition from paternalism to patient-centred care occurred over a relatively short period of time. To illustrate this timeframe, in 1970 the BMA ran a poster campaign called *'Be a patient'*, which essentially meant that the patient should listen to, and accept what their doctors told them. Around 30 years later BUPA issued a campaign, *'The patient will see you now, Doctor'* illustrating the shifting power in the doctor-patient relationship. The doctor has now become a service for the patient to utilise rather than an authority for them to obey.

Mentor's Tip

*There are still issues with doctor-patient equality in hospital settings. **Dr Kate Granger** is an NHS consultant but is also a patient with terminal cancer. She observed her treatment as a patient through the eyes of a doctor and was shocked to find out that doctors did not introduce themselves to her when they addressed her. This limits the rapport between doctor and patient and negates their on-going relationship. Dr Granger reflected on her experience of this by saying, "The lack of introductions really made me feel like just a diseased body and not a real person." Consequently, she started the #Hello My Name Is... campaign in hospitals to get doctors to introduce themselves to patients and make them feel less dehumanised.*

Food for Thought: *Do you think the drive for patient-centred care has raised patient expectations of the NHS and their doctors? How would you address this change in expectations?*

Write your answer here:

Ethical Dilemma: Can you think of any situations when paternalism is beneficial?

Write your answer here:

Arguably, public health is the last bastion of paternalism in 21st century healthcare. Many people feel that they should be able to make their own lifestyle decisions regarding what they eat, how much they exercise and other lifestyle choices without the interference of organisations such as Public Health England. Public Health England has the challenge of balancing perceived benefits of policies with the public's and opposing bodies' views; for example, the 2007 smoking ban which was opposed by the Tobacco industry. The policy seemed like a good idea, due to the potential health improvement benefits, however it received heavy opposition from a group called 'Freedom to Choose', who stated that the ban was a violation of their human rights.

The King's Fund, an organisation that conducts health related research, produced a document titled, *"Nanny or Steward – the Government's role in Public health"*, which addresses this contentious issue. The study looked at whether the government acts as a 'nanny' who is intrusive of our lives or if they act as a 'steward' who has a responsibility to protect the health of the country. The tone of the report seems to support a role of the government as a steward and it states that depending on the situation, it may be acceptable for the government to act as a paternalistic steward to achieve certain health improvements. The line between these two roles, nanny and steward, is subjective and ultimately, the level of involvement public health organisations have in our day-to-day lives will depend on what society deems is appropriate. Although people should be free to run their own lives their lifestyle choices can raise ethical dilemmas.

Ethical Dilemma: *Should obese people be allowed bariatric surgery considering the huge pressures on the NHS budget is?*

Write your answer here:

Ethical Dilemma: *Should obese children be given priority to bariatric surgery over the obese elderly?*

Write your answer here:

Ethical Dilemma: Should alcoholics be given a liver transplant when the waiting list for transplants is so high?

Write your answer here:

Ethical Dilemma: Should people who have had a transplant rejection because they did not fully adhered to their immunosuppressants, be allowed another transplant? Regarding organ transplantation, public health leaders have an important question to consider: would it be beneficial to change to an opt-out system from the current opt-in system?

Write your answer here:

In the UK you currently have to sign up to the organ transplant register. In an opt-out system you will have to apply to not be part of the system. The logic is that changing the system will increase the number of organs for transplantation. This is because some people are not against the idea of transplantation but find it too much hassle to register as a donor in an opt-in system. Once again in this scenario the public may regard this change in policy restrictive, and think it is unfair that they have to apply to keep their organs.

A movement that is gaining momentum, which could benefit the health of the population without making public health entities appear paternalistic, is the social norms approach. Traditionally, health promotion material would identify the damaging effects of smoking on health and the problems with binge drinking in an effort to shock the public into stopping these unhealthy activities. These are somewhat counterintuitive as they give the perception that more people are engaging in these activities than actually are. The social norms approach addresses these misperceptions and takes a less offensive stance. An example could be *"did you know that over 95% of Trenton college students do not smoke cigarettes"* as opposed to a social marketing campaign which might state *"second- hand smoking: your cigarettes are not just killing you they are killing your children too"*. The latter campaign reflects the victim-blaming approach in medicine, where the doctor would blame the patient for their smoking habits in an attempt to get them to quit – a method already proved to be ineffective.

The Rise of the Three Parent Babies

'Three parent babies' are being discussed extensively in the media. The underlying scientific method known as mitochondrial donation was legalised in the UK in early 2015. The UK is currently the only country to legalise the procedure. It is thought that the first of these three parent babies could be born in 2016. The term three-parent baby is rather misleading, and has been criticised by scientists as tabloid sensationalism, as the babies born from the procedure share over 99% of their DNA with two parents – their mother and father. The main difference between three parent babies and conventional birth babies is that the child receives their mitochondrial DNA from a donor rather than their mother.

Mitochondria are cell organelles that are essential for energy generation through cellular metabolism. They are essentially the power plants of our cells. Most of our DNA is stored in our cell nucleus, called nuclear DNA however mitochondria have their own mitochondrial DNA, which reflects the endosymbiotic theory: this states that mitochondria were once free-living organisms and at one stage were engulfed, and incorporated into another organism. After millions of years of evolution leading up to genesis of humanity, mitochondrial DNA has remained distinct from nuclear DNA.

Mitochondria DNA codes for 37 genes out of approximately 20,000 – 25,000 genes in the human genome, that's approximately 0.2% of coding DNA. Importantly, mitochondrial DNA only codes for metabolic processes not physical characteristics. Mitochondrial DNA is only inherited from a child's mother and this causes difficulties for mothers with mitochondrial diseases, who want to have children. If a mother has a mitochondrial disease all her children will have the disease whereas if a father has a mitochondrial disease none of his children will have the disease. As many as 1 in 200 children are born with mitochondrial defects, which can result in symptoms such as muscular weakness and movement problems and lead to diseases such as diabetes and deafness. These defects are not curable and sometimes fatal. If a child were born with the mitochondrial DNA of a healthy donor but the nuclear DNA of their parents, then they would be genetically their parent's child but not inherit the disease – cue mitochondrial donation.

Mitochondrial donation uses a modified version of in vitro fertilisation (IVF). In IVF the mother's egg is fertilised by the father's sperm outside of her body and it is later implanted into the mother's uterus. The process of mitochondrial donation can be done through two methods. The Maternal spindle transfer method removes the mother's nuclear DNA from her egg cell and inserts it into a donor egg cell, which has had its nucleus removed. This donor cell now contains the mitochondrial DNA of the donor and the nucleus of the mother. This egg will then be fertilised and implanted via IVF. The other method called the pronuclear method, involves fertilisation of both eggs before the nuclear DNA is transferred. Both methods have been successfully used in animal models to produce offspring without mitochondrial defects and have been tested in the laboratories to produce healthy human embryos. Multiple expert reviews have also deemed the process as safe.

ARGUMENTS FOR	ARGUMENTS AGAINST
• Allows women to have genetic children without passing on debilitation defects. • Helps to remove a genetic defect from the gene pool. • It is immoral to not prevent disease if possible. • It could save the lives of a child born with a potentially lethal metabolic disorder. • It only requires substituted mitochondrial DNA which codes for metabolic processes and not personal characteristics. • Over 99% of the child's DNA will be inherited from the parents so it is essentially a two parent baby. • If it is seen as ethically acceptable for couples to have children through IVF, then why not through mitochondrial donation as they	• No human clinical trials have been done- only animal models. • Mitochondrial DNA may later be found to affect our characteristics in a way we could not determine in animals. • There may be some unknown harmful epigenetic effects from the process. • It isn't natural fertilisation and it is playing God. • It leads to unnatural modification of the germline (genetic changes that are passed on to subsequent generations) and it is a step on the slippery slope to designer babies and eugenics. • Potential psychological implications for children - who do they identify as their parents? Do they feel different to everyone else? • Pronuclear method destroys the mother's fertilised embryo - some people feel that this is taking a life.

Figure 3: Arguments for and Against Mitochondrial Donation

The mentors have tried to present the information in an as balance way as possible but in general the pros seem to greatly outweigh the cons, reflecting the general public, scientific and medical support for mitochondrial donation.

Any advancement in medical technology that affects human genetics understandably raises ethical concerns. The process of mitochondrial donation is irreversible and its effects will echo down generations. Some people consider this as a step on the slippery slope to designer babies and eugenics. However scientists argue against this stating that creation of designer babies would require modification of nuclear DNA, which is still banned by law, and mitochondrial donation only affects metabolic processes not physical traits. Some representatives of the Catholic Church have argued that mitochondrial donation might dilute parenthood. Although this point of view has been refuted considering how small a percentage of DNA the children inherit from the donor. Some critics have speculated that epigenetic differences may cause a problem. Epigenetics involves changing the expression of the gene (whether the gene is turned on or turned off); it doesn't change the genetic code. However there has been no evidence to support this speculation. The main arguments for and against mitochondrial donation have been summarised in the Figure 3.

Ethical Dilemma: Do you feel that mitochondrial donation is acceptable or is a step too far?

Write your answer here:

Food for Thought: Do you think the donor should have any say in the child's life?

Write your answer here:

Food for Thought: If mitochondrial donation was later found to have some effect on personality or physical traits would you feel that this was too far? Would it be ethical to go back once some 3-parent children were already born?

Write your answer here:

Food for Thought: Do you think it is a step in the right direction and we have more progress to make? Do you think that we should be able to edit nuclear DNA to prevent genetic conditions such as Cystic Fibrosis being passed on?

Write your answer here:

Telomerases are enzymes in our body that reverse the shortening of Telomeres, repetitive sequences of DNA which act as caps preventing the ends of our chromosomes from breaking down. Telomeres shorten after a cell cycle, the process where one cell divides mitotically into two. A study in 2012 used telomerase gene therapy on 1-year-old mice and found that it increased mean lifespan by 24% - these results could one day be replicated in humans...

Controversy in the NHS

Possibly the most controversial change in the NHS was the Health and Social Care Act 2012, discussed in the chapter on NHS Structure and Policy. Since then there have been several other topics, which have put the NHS in the spotlight. A couple of prominent examples are the A&E waiting times and health tourism.

In 2004 the UK Labour Government assigned a four-hour waiting time target for Accident and Emergency departments across the country to address their underperformance. This required that 98% of A&E must see and discharge, transfer or admit a patient to the ward within four hours of arrival. This target was later adjusted to 95% of departments in 2010 by the coalition government as doctors felt this target was compromising decision-making. By 2006, 98.2% of departments hit the targets, between January and March 2015 this had fallen to 91.8%, the lowest level in a decade. Research group Quality Watch stated that the problems were due to the rising demand of an aging population and population growth, outweighing the already stretched service. The BMA expressed that failings were due to a lack of inpatient beds, not enough healthcare staff and delayed discharges, amongst other reasons. A major problem A&E departments are facing is the number of patients using the service with non-urgent problems. The King's Fund found that only about 60% of patients attending A&E departments require emergency treatment. This means that there is a considerable number of patients, who may be unnecessarily using A&E services. This may be partially accounted for by the issues in accessing GP services. Furthermore, a recent survey showed that only around 50% of patients knew how to use GP out of hours services, which may also contribute to unnecessary A&E usage.

Ethical Dilemma: *Should people whom inappropriately use A&E services have to pay?*

Write your answer here:

Ethical Dilemma: *How would you define misuse of services?*

Write your answer here:

Inappropriate use of A&E services is being tackled by the NHS's Choose Well campaign. This health promotion campaign categorises ailments and injuries and tells the patient, which service is most appropriate for their situation. For example, grazes should be treated by self-care, emergency contraception is available from pharmacists and for suspected fractures you should go to A&E.

Health or medical tourism is a phrase that has been used a lot, particularly in the 2015 government election period. Medical tourism involves people travelling from their country of origin to another country to utilise its healthcare services. It is something that is increasing year on year, partly owed to the increase in globalisation and decrease in travel costs. Traditionally, health tourists would travel from less economically developed countries to more economically developed countries. Recently, the reverse trend is occurring. There are various reasons why medical tourism occurs:

Some countries offer healthcare free at the point of delivery such as the United Kingdom.	Some countries offer cheaper healthcare services than others – Thailand is comparably cheaper than the USA.
Some countries have better healthcare provisions and technologies – the USA are leaders in the field of robotic surgery.	Some countries permit medical procedures that others will not. For example, abortion is illegal in the Republic of Ireland but not in the United Kingdom.

Figure 4: Reasons for Medical Tourism

This figure summarises 4 main reasons why people travel abroad for healthcare.

Some ethical concerns arise with health tourism:

- Health tourism may widen the gap in health inequalities as health tourists are utilising the destination country's limited resources;

- Tourists may return to their country of origin with antibiotic-resistant infections compromising the health of their community;

- There are always risks to patient's health when they travel abroad ill;

- Doctors may not be able to access foreign patient's medical documentation which could compromise their quality of care.

The UK Health minister Jeremy Hunt proposed a £200 charge for temporary migrants to use the NHS, however Clare Gerada, ex-chair of the Royal College of GPs stated that this system would actually cost the NHS more to implement than would be saved from charging them.

Food for Thought: *Should the UK provide abortions to people whose country of origin prohibits the procedure?*

Write your answer here:

Food for Thought: *Should the US government further subsidise healthcare costs so US citizens do not feel the need to go abroad for treatment?*

Write your answer here:

Food for Thought: *Is it worth travelling across the globe for potentially better treatment?* Consider the costs of health tourism for the patient including (this is not an expansive list):

Financial: will it cost more to travel to another country than the patient will save from receiving treatment in their country of origin?

Health-related: Potential development of illnesses during travel. For example, deep vein thrombosis on long-haul flights.

Sociocultural: will women who travel to another country to have an abortion be rejected by their community on returning home?

There have been varying estimates of how much health tourism costs the UK in the media ranging from around £100,000,000 to £2,000,000,000. The actual figure for treating ill/injured people who intentionally travel to the UK to use NHS services is around £100,000,000 to £300,000,000. In terms of the NHS budget this is around 0.1%- 0.3%. Around £1,800,000,000 is spent treating 'non-British nationals' in the UK – these are not the same as health tourists. Non-British nationals include immigrants, people on working visas, international students and expats, who fall ill or are injured whilst in the country. Although 1.8 billion pounds seems to be a considerable figure this still only forms around 2% of the NHS total budget and it is thought that up to about 500 million pounds for these procedures may be recoverable. These figures do not account for the money made from health tourists who pay for treatments. In the grand scheme of things, health tourism is only a minor problem for the NHS, which has been distorted through political spin.

Junior doctor contracts

In 2013, the British Medical Association (BMA – doctors' trade union), NHS Employers and the Department of Health (i.e. the government), began discussing the structure and implementation of a new NHS contract; for all non-general practice doctors in training below consultant level. Unfortunately, communications broke down in 2015, with the government pushing to unilaterally impose it's chosen contract, whilst the junior doctors elected to go on strike after being balloted by the BMA.

It seems that the strikes had little effect, as the government started imposing the contract in 2016. In the same year, the BMA stepped back from further strike action and re-balloted its members on the new contract structure. 58% rejected it and 42% accepted it. This followed assurances from the Secretary of State for Health and Social Care, Jeremy Hunt, stating that the overall pay packet for junior doctors would remain unchanged.

Officially, the BMA still appears to reject the contract, as per its mandate of 58% of its members rejecting it. In practice, junior doctors can either work, 'under protest' and not sign their contract, or just continue to work as normal. Since the implementation of the new contract, the number of post-FY2 doctors, going into recognized training posts has dropped significantly, to less than half of eligible candidates. To be fair, the numbers have been dropping for the best part of a decades, and we have to consider both the push factors of the NHS environment (including the contract), and the pull factors of working and training abroad – you generally get paid more for less hours in Australia for example, but training posts are often harder to come by; especially in competitive specialties.

Three years on, the junior doctor contract remains a current healthcare issue. This is simply because doctors are now either working subject to this contract or they may continue to avoid training as a direct result of its continued implementation. Unfortunately, there are many other factors that might be confounding its effect, including exotic foreign options, Brexit and the current UK economic climate. It is also important to remember that the primary concern of doctors and the BMA (on their behalf), was widely regarded to be one of patient (and doctor) safety. Yes, there was also immediate concern in relation to recognized pay decreases (albeit with pay protection and ultimate earning potential allegedly unchanged – time will tell).

Removing monitoring and replacing it with the guardian system has had much negative press, at the time. There was significant concern from doctors that this new system would lead to them consistently working longer hours – more than they were paid for but also more than was safe. Many doctors explained how they would stay late or come in early to make sure patients were well cared for, because this is in the nature of caring individuals. Some said that this sense of goodwill was propping up the NHS and would be exploited further under the new Guardian system, as doctors would now have to justify shift overruns and their guardian would have to determine whether this was a result of personal altruism or a real need to support an inefficient system. There was also concern, that the government had not taken into account and indeed was not able to accurately measure the amount of additional 'goodwill' hours put in by doctors, and other healthcare staff. It was suggested by many front-line workers that they were changing a system that they did not actually have all the data for.

That was then (2016); from now (2018 onwards), what we are seeing more of is an issue with low staffing levels, increased waiting times, missed A&E targets, and mistakes being made on the front line. Could this be the culmination of the safety concerns the doctors and the BMA had warned of? Are doctors (and other healthcare staff) putting in fewer of these goodwill hours or are the staffing levels just so low that even with extra unpaid time, we cannot meet the needs of our expanding population? Logic would suggest that there is a mixture of these things happening – but how and what do we measure, and can it be changed?

You can find out more about the junior doctor contract issue from both government and BMA websites. Be aware however, that these sides were at times, diametrically opposed to each other and both had contrasting approaches to the disagreement. Usefully impartial information can be found at FullFact.org – the UK's independent factchecking charity. A direct link to a helpful summary page is listed in the Further Reading section at the end of this book, but it also comes up on a simple web search. A final caveat to this section is that Medic Mentor is essentially an organizations of healthcare professionals, whose opinions are also more likely to align with organisations that advocate for other healthcare professionals. For the purposes of personal statements and medical school interviews, you need to impartially assess evidence and to formulate your own arguments on this; to work what is safe and best practice, with the information you have and on the balance of probability.

More than just an issue with doctors and their contracts?

If you read some media pieces, there seems to be a much deeper and longer term issue in relation to funding and prioritization of the NHS. Many of these articles are actually supported by real data, which seems to substantiate their positions quite convincingly: a quick glance at some statistics from the King's Fund, shows how the UK spends less on its health service than all other European countries listed, in relation to its GDP (Gross Domestic Product, aka UK yearly income). Interestingly, this also includes spending on private healthcare alongside tax-funded NHS care. You could argue that the NHS is a super-efficient system and needs relatively less funding than other countries, although this would need to be supported by evidence. This could perhaps be where goodwill hours come in, but they are very difficult to quantify. When researching this issue, it would be wise to look for statistics that support any assertions or opinions you come across, be they from the lay media, doctors organisations or government sources.

Taking a longer-term look at total spending on healthcare, there has clearly been decreasing year-upon-year, GDP-relative funding since 2009 (again according to the King's fund). This appears to roughly coincide with the policies of austerity, which followed shortly after the recession, and importantly pre-dated the junior doctors' contract issue which started in 2013. There are clearly multiple facts that affect the end working conditions in the NHS: contracts (hours, pay, conditions, teaching), the number and health of patients, and the amount of money available for staff and services. It could be argued that the overall picture is what ultimately matters to prospective workers. For example, if a highly qualified doctor perceives that working conditions are not favourable, they might 'vote with their feet' and set up shop in an Australian emergency department; working 40 hours per weeks for more money than they would get for working far more hours in the NHS. No matter what protestations the government and NHS England make about how fair the new deal is for doctors, it remains difficult from promises and rhetoric to convince an independent group of professionals who are taught to critically analyze data from undergraduate level.

That said, many point to the fact that most doctors remain in the UK and the NHS.
We should not take this as implicit support for current NHS policies however. Many doctors remain for family, personal and other reasons – some of them believe that the NHS will weather the storm, as it has for the past 20 years; politicians, policies and governments continue to change. When dealing with highly educated, motivated individuals who can just as easily become victims of unrelated circumstances, we should be careful not to draw conclusion too quickly. That is the remit of politics, not science, healthcare or medicine. For the purposes of medical school interviews therefore, maintaining an open mind is paramount. Beyond regurgitating facts and figures, you should also demonstrate an ability to empathise with doctors and consider your own opinions on the environment in which you have elected to work in the future.

Food for Thought: *Was the junior doctor contract issue simply a byproduct of austerity? What do you think the primary concerns of doctors are, regarding the new contract? What would you do if you had just finished your foundation training?*

Write your answer here:

Food for Thought: *With the benefit of hindsight, were the government actually right to impose the new contract and was it perhaps in the best interests of doctors and patients? If not then why? Justify your position with facts and opinions. Use data, logic and common sense – and ethical arguments!*

Write your answer here:

Mistakes and medical manslaughter – the Bawa Garba case

The Hadiza Bawa-Garba case, and indeed that of her nursing counterpart Isabel Amaro, made national headlines recently. This concerned the preventable death of a 6-year-old boy, called Jack Adcock. Jack had Trisomy 21 (Down's Syndrome) and a heart condition. He was referred to a Children's Assessment Unit by his GP and admitted under the medical care of Dr. Hadiza Bawa-Garba. She was a (relatively senior) junior doctor, recently returned from maternity leave and actually on her first shift. There were reported problems with hospital IT services, causing delay to blood results and radiology scans. Jack's treatment for sepsis was sub-optimal (as later decided by the court) and he died an hour or so after receiving his heart medication, which was not prescribed.

This case has so many complicating factors. Here are a few listed below:

1) Jack was not prescribed his heart medication but this was given by his mother, apparently in accordance with hospital policy.

2) Dr. Bawa-Garba did not prescribe this medication but questions were raised as to whether she made it clear enough, that it was not to be given.

3) There was delay in treatment (antibiotics) for Jack's sepsis.

4) Allegedly, Dr. Bawa-Garba was doing the work of more than one doctor, dealing with IT failures and an unusually large through flow of patients.

5) There was also the factor of consultant review. There remains confusion as to whether Jack should have been reviewed by the senior doctor on call; he was very sick but his results were improving. Dr. Bawa-Garba apparently also did not explicitly ask for a review.

6) In terms of the legal decision, the courts apparently took these environmental factors into account, and she was still deemed to have provided suboptimal care.

7) She was convicted of gross negligence manslaughter, alongside (albeit separately to), Nurse Isabel Amaro.

Following Jack's death, things got even more complicated. Dr. Bawa-Garba continued to work from 2011, with no other reported incidents. She was convicted of gross negligence manslaughter in 2015 and given a 24-month suspended sentence. She was denied leave to appeal this in 2016. In June 2017, the Medical Practitioners Tribunal Service (MPTS), decided to go against the advice of its own parent body, the General Medical Council, and refused to strike off the doctor. Instead she was given a 12-month suspension, as erasure was considered disproportionate. Incidentally, the MPTS combines a mixture of legal and medical professionals, and is used specifically when a case (like this) blurs the lines between legal precedent and professional practice. The idea is that the judgement of the panel combines both perspectives, in a real-world application.

Weirdly, the GMC took its own dedicated subsidiary, the MPTS, to the High Court to push for the permanent erasure of Dr. Bawa Garba, from the medical register. The GMC was successful and Hadiza Bawa-Garba ceased to be a practicing doctor on 25th January 2018. The rationale behind this court action seems to be that the GMC thought suspension and subsequent return to work, did not accurately reflect the level of culpability placed upon Dr. Bawa-Garba. There also seems to be an inherent implication that someone who is convicted of Manslaughter is not fit to be a doctor, or that Hadiza Bawa Garba was otherwise deemed to be a danger to the public and a patient safety risk. Incidentally, these justifications (for the GMC's push for erasure), would have been refuted by the MPTS when they recommended only suspension; the clear implication being that after this 12-month period, they saw no reason why Dr. Bawa-Garba could not return to clinical practice as a safe and competent doctor.

Interestingly, the ultimate erasure decision was taken by a lay jury (under the guidance of the High Court judge), rather than by a dedicated mixed-professional panel of individuals with specific and relevant insight. Given the emotional nature of a case where a 6-year-old child has died as a result of suboptimal care, many people have voiced concerns about the objectivity of this judgement. Personal opinions aside, the law remains the law and the only way to challenge this decision is via and appeals process – just like the one that was previously denied for her conviction of gross negligence manslaughter. For now, Dr. Bawa-Garba remains erased from the medical register.

Things got even more strange in 2018, when it transpired that Dr. Bawa-Garba's personal reflections may have been used against her in court, during her trial for gross negligence manslaughter. There were further questions in the media as to whether there was any inherent discrimination, based upon race and religion, in the processes that took place. Following this, her case was taken up by a crowd-funding group, who was supporting another junior doctor on an unrelated issue (although Chris Day's case does potentially overlap with the larger issue of patient safety in the NHS). Hadiza Bawa-Garba has since been granted leave to appeal against here conviction for gross negligence manslaughter...after having been refused this very route initially. Her case has been re-assessed and now seems to meet all the legal test for an appeal. If Dr. Bawa-Garba's conviction is quashed, this sheds doubt upon the GMC/High Court decision to remove her from the medical register. Theoretically both judgments could be overturned. They could also remain in place if her appeals process(es) are not successful.

Food for Thought: Is it right to punish individual members of a team who work in a technology and staff-based environment, when both technology and staffing levels are suboptimal?

Write your answer here:

This case is fraught with legal, professional and lay concepts (largely in the media). The situation is emotionally charged, involving the death of a disabled child, the mourning of a family, the loss of two professionals' careers and potentially endemic racism and discrimination. You will not be expected to have definitive answers to these issues therefore as even specifically trained professionals appear to disagree on many of the points. You will stand out however, if you can demonstrate an affinity for information gathering and you are able to process complex issues into a chronological, overall picture. You can apply ethical principles and some knowledge of relevant legislature (see Chapter 3) to model this scenario and come to your own reasoned conclusions.

Food for Thought: Should doctors and nurses remain professionally and independently responsible for their actions, irrespective of environmental factors? Alternatively: these professionals are specifically trained to deal with life and death situations under high pressure, so when patients die should they be culpable because they failed to do what they were trained for?

Write your answer here:

Whistleblowing in the NHS

Whistleblowing normally refers to a confidential, anonymous or protected method of raising concerns in an organization. The idea is that the concerns can be addressed without the individual who raised them being blamed or compromised in any way. Theoretically, section 43K of the Employment Rights Act 1996 (see Further Reading section), provides statutory whistleblowing protection to all individuals, from their employers. In practice for junior doctors, there has been an confusion as to who the employment organization is: The postgraduate deanery, which is part of Health Education England (HEE), or the trust within which a doctor works. Theoretically a trust could agree for a doctor to work but HEE can independently remove or refuse to allocate a training number – preventing a doctor from taking up a post that is designated for training. The doctor could still work in a non-training post, with the consent of the employing trust however. This is essentially what happened to Chris Day.

Chris Day

In 2014, Dr. Christopher Day was working as a junior doctor in an Intensive Care Unit (ICU). He became concerned about low staffing levels and the potential effect on patient safety. He raised a concern with his trust and a series of unfortunate events ensued. He found himself with negative official reports in his end of year review, which he was unable to conscionably accept on his record. This led to a non-compliance with HEE procedures and the termination of his job at the time and his training pathway towards becoming a consultant.

Dr. Day has since worked as a doctor in non-training posts, whilst simultaneously pursuing legal actions to clear his record and reinstate his training number. In May 2018, he won a Court of Appeal judgement confirming that HEE is indeed a secondary employer of junior doctors (and dentists) in training. Therefore these individuals' whistleblowing actions are protected under Section 43K of the Employment Rights Act 1996. Chris faces a further challenge to have his individual case heard, in relation to a claim of constructive dismissal as a result of his own whistleblowing actions.

Food for Thought: Why is whistleblowing important in an organization? What are the potential benefits for the NHS, patients and doctors? Can you think of any other examples of whistleblowing in healthcare? What were the outcomes?

Write your answer here:

Chapter 3: Medical Ethics and Law

Mentor's Tip

This chapter has been designed so the concepts are easy to understand, easy to recall and easy to apply. There are detailed examples to reinforce your learning, with discussion of conflicting ethical and legal issues. Essentially, medical ethics and law are all about applying the same principles to different situations – once you have seen a few landmark legal cases, and absorbed some basic ethical theory, you should be able to work out how to act in similar scenarios. For practice interview questions with worked answers, please refer to Medic Mentor's Interview Skills Checklists or visit www.medicmentor.org for more details.

You will likely first encounter ethico-legal scenarios on your medical work experience, so it helps to have a basic working knowledge of these subjects. Additionally, when you are writing your personal statement, reflecting upon ethico-legal situations can communicate additional insight into a medical career. Arguably the biggest challenge is when you are faced with these types of scenarios at interview.

Most resources go into quite a lot of detail regarding medical ethics and law. You will find long-winded descriptions of the origins of ethical, moral and legal practice, from the dawn of civilisation. This level of knowledge is excessive and therefore not essential to the medical application process. All you really need to know about are the fundamentals of ethical practice and the impact of major health legislation (health-related laws), upon modern healthcare.

With respect to interviews, ethico-legal questions all tend to follow a similar format. You will have to interpret a situation; applying logic and reason, leading you to justifiable decisions or actions. Alternatively, you may have to judge available actions or rank them against each other in terms of appropriateness - so-called 'situational judgement testing'.

Whatever style the interviewers use, you should have analysed and evaluated the situation and discussed the merits and drawbacks of all potential actions. Your reasoning should be spoken out loud to get full marks and you must also make a final action decision. Not considering all options; not explaining your reasoning and not making action decisions will lose you marks. A logical approach model for answering questions, will be discussed later in this chapter.

It is important to note that many situations present ethico-legal dilemmas that have no obvious answer or perhaps several equally valid ones. This can cause distress at the interview if you are grasping for the 'correct answer' – it simply may not exist. The interviewers are fully aware of this and often deliberately chose scenarios that are open to interpretation. It is for this reason that you must clearly highlight your reasoning and state the ethical and legal concepts you are drawing upon. You will also find that as many marks are available for your thought process for the final decision. Fundamentally, medical interviewers are looking for candidates who make logical, safe and well-justified action choices; these candidates are more likely to be safe, thoughtful and insightful doctors.

Basic Concepts

What are Ethics?

You can think of ethics collectively as a system or moral code that can be used to arrive at appropriate decisions. Classically, ethical and moral reasoning have been linked to religious teaching and traditional philosophical arguments. Ethics help us to take actions that benefit individuals and populations as much as possible. Of the many ethical schools of thought, modern healthcare or 'bioethics', has adopted a system based around fundamental principles. The theory is that these principles help to guide our decision making in a way that is respectful, beneficial, prevents harm; that is fair and within legal parameters. In fact, the clues are in the names of these principles.

Fundamental ethical principles

1)   **Autonomy** – respecting the wishes of the individual and/or patient.

2)   **Beneficence** – working according to the best interests of the patient (as determined by parties other than the patient).

3)   **Non-maleficence** – preventing or averting harm to the patient. In practice, this includes reducing existing harm, minimizing unavoidable harm and substituting relatively more harmful actions for less harmful ones (if the harm cannot be avoided and is in keeping with other principles).

4)   **Justice** – working within a framework that promotes fairness and equality. This principle overlaps with and is often based upon legal limitations, landmark cases and prescribed guidelines. Justice, via the law, is also responsible for protecting individuals and organisations from harm.

Confidentiality – a Fifth Fundamental Ethical Principle?

There is no legal requirement for a doctor to maintain confidentiality. Its maintenance is largely rooted in ethical practice. Although it is not a classical fundamental principle, it has been included here as it is an integral part of the doctor-patient relationship. Most lay people (non-healthcare professionals) are aware of 'doctor-patient confidentiality' and there is an expectation that your personal information will not be divulged unnecessarily. Indeed, the General Medical Council (GMC – UK professional regulator of doctors) requires all doctors to act with, 'openness, honesty and integrity'. In every day practice, a patient's 'right to confidentiality' (although not a legal right), is protected under the GMC's, 'duties of a doctor...', which forms part of the overarching professional guideline called Good Medical Practice (see further reading section at the end of this book). In theory, the ramifications of breaching confidentiality unnecessarily, are also potential harm to a patient and negligence as a result of breaching duty of care (under the Law of Tort – more in this later). So confidentiality then, although it has no specific law enforcing it, is encircled by ethics, professional standards and related legislation.

Notwithstanding these factors, doctors effectively have to break confidentiality on a regular basis when they refer patients to colleagues, different specialties, professions or organisations. Ideally this is done with the consent of the patient (thereby respecting autonomy) and actually extending the confidentiality bubble, but this is not always practicable. Doctors classically share information to support patient diagnosis or management, and it is therefore in the patient's best interest and usually reduces harm (non-maleficence).

There are also some legal limitations when it comes to written and computer based information, such as blood tests and patient notes. These come under the remit of the Data Protection Act 1998. Data has to be kept on secure servers and can only be accessed by approved personnel. Likewise, patient notes are kept securely on wards or a records department. All organisations who keep personal data, have to b registered with the Information Commissioners' Office (ICO), for Data Protection. Nowadays, we have the new General Data Protection Regulation (GDPR) rules, which require organisations that hold private personal data (anything from names and addresses upwards), to prove why they need to have this information and that they have permission to use it for a specific purpose. There are also additional protection put in place for dealing with at risk or vulnerable populations, and specifically their data and communicating with them (See wider reading section at the end of this book).

There are some situations where a patient's right to confidentiality is directly compromised. For example if they are a risk to the public (or themselves) and need to be sectioned. In which case their data can be shared with the police. Or if they are involved in an ongoing criminal investigation, in which case the police might request their details of their treatment from the emergency department, for example. These situations are carefully regulated and requests for confidential information are usually written and authorized in advance. This is to prevent people from calling or appearing without identification, and taking confidential data from an NHS database – hence breaching the Data Protection Act 1988.

You may recall the sad case of the nurse who divulged data about Kate Middleton's pregnancy, to a couple of radio show hosts claiming to be members of the Royal family. One of the nurses involved eventually took her own life, underscoring the seriousness of the issue and also perhaps the level of care and commitment felt by healthcare professionals. There is also a concern here about support for nurses and doctors who make mistakes; an easily overlooked area when we are so strongly encouraged to focus upon the rights of the patient. Perhaps for this reason, many interview questions and MMI stations place a high weighting on the demonstration of team-working and support for colleagues in difficult situations. You should actively look out for this during your work experience and volunteering placements.

Professional Objectivity and Senior Guidance

In amongst all of this ethical reasoning, you may find that you develop personal opinions on certain issues. This is human nature but doctors are also required to maintain a professional objectivity. That is not to say that you should not empathise with patients however. In situations that are ethically uncertain (and there are no trust or professional guidelines), you should discuss the case with your seniors or with a medical defence organisation such as the Medical Defence Union (MDU) or the Medical Protection Society (MPS). All doctors are required to be registered with one of these organisations, which provide medico-legal support to clinicians. They also provide legal support to doctors who may be facing a lawsuit (e.g. medical negligence). There is more information about medically related organisations in the chapter, 'significant organisations'.

Doctor-doctor Disputes and Conflicts with your Employing Trust

All of the discussion so far has been about ethical issues relating to patients and with doctors as their champions. It is also possible to have differing opinions with your colleagues or with guidance from your employer. Again you should refer to the MPS or MDU for ethico-legal guidance. This is because even if you follow senior advice in treating a patient, you are still responsible for your individual actions. Doctors are expected to be independently competent and you are required (by the GMC) to promote patient safety by raising any concerns that you have with proposed treatments or management plans.

If you have concerns relating to your treatment by your employers, then this represents a different ethical dilemma. If you are working too many hours, or you have issues with your professional contract for example, these issues are not normally covered by the MDU or MPS. They can still represent ethical issues as working more hours than you are contracted for example, can affect professional performance and impact upon patient safety (non-maleficence). Your first port of call for work-related issues such as this, is the doctors' trade union, the British Medical Association (BMA). You could also seek independent legal advice, or consider an employment tribunal, if you feel you have been discriminated against by your employer. Naturally, all cases in these situations will be individual and so individual research would be required into the appropriate organisations to help you. For the purposes of interview questions, you must demonstrate the potential for safe practice; you know whom and or which organization to contact, in a time of particular stress, to maintain the safety of yourself, your patient and your team.

What is the Law and how does it differ from Ethics?

You are not expected to have detailed legal understanding or a long list of memorised cases, although should you need to refer to these the MDU and the MPS produce regular case studies. You can also view fundamental law on the legislation.gov.uk website. Any interpretation or application of this to a specific case or person would require independent legal advice however.

Remember that your primary focus should be the application of knowledge in interviews (and in your personal statement). Basic legal knowledge also helps to contextualise your work experience, allowing you to understand the actions of doctors in relation to patients. Essentially, you can think of the law as a set of rules that we are all bound by in this country, whereas ethics are there to guide us. Unfortunately, there is clear overlap between ethics and law, as you will read shortly. In the case of breaching ethical principles (or GMC professional standards), there may also be legal ramifications (e.g. medical negligence).

Focusing on the law for now, this tends to state absolutes and lines that cannot be crossed, without severe penalties. For example, fraud, murder and theft. The application of law in healthcare is usually related to the provision (or withholding) of healthcare services. It is primarily based upon the Law of Tort, which means it is decided upon the 'balance of probabilities'. In a murder case, a defendant's guilt has to be proven 'beyond all reasonable doubt'; in a case where a doctor is being accused of negligence there only needs to be sufficient evidence to suggest it was 'more likely' that they were negligent.

The concept of negligence is based upon a doctor's 'duty of care'. This is a legal standpoint where, when an individual becomes a doctor's responsibility (as their patient), the doctor is then legally bound to look after them, to the best of their ability and within universally accepted professional standards (set by the GMC). This can be in the form of diagnosis, treatment, medication, surgery, counselling or other healthcare services. If any of these are denied or withdrawn from a patient (who is owed a duty of care by their doctor) and without good reason, the doctor could have breached their duty of care and be held as negligent.

You can see how the legal concepts of 'duty of care' and 'negligence' are also related to the ethical principles of 'beneficence' and 'non-maleficence'. These in turn also have specific legal underpinnings. Beneficence is linked to 'Common Law', non-maleficence is related to the Human Rights Act and the Offenses Against the Person Act.

Common Law/Case Law and Legal Precedents

In some situations, there are no specific laws to govern a doctor's actions but there is legal case history. You may find that individual cases are used to formulate 'legal guidelines' and to form a legal precedent. A good example of this is, 'Gillick Vs West Norfolk and Wisbech Area Health Authority 1984-5'. This legal case went to the House of Lords and resulted in the Fraser Guidelines for under-16 assessment of capacity in relation to contraception prescriptions. We will talk more about this example later.

Logical Approach to Practical Ethico-legal Scenarios and Interview Questions

To help you consolidate your thoughts and to demonstrate logic and reason, you can use the following three-step approach:

1) **Situational analysis** – what are the issues; spell it out to get the marks?

   - What legal concepts are involved e.g. competence and capacity?
   - What ethical principles are involved e.g. autonomy and beneficence?

2) **Situational evaluation** – what is good and what is bad?

   - How do the situation and the proposed actions support or come into conflict with these ethical principles and legal concepts?
   - For example, do they respect autonomy, promote beneficence or fulfill a doctor's duty of care?
   - Alternatively, are these actions potentially harmful or do they contravene certain laws or rights (like the Human Rights Act)?

3) **Conclusions and comparative justifications** – what would you do and why?

   - Rank actions in terms of ethical and legal suitability.
   - Suggest the most appropriate option or your chosen course of action.
   - Suggest the least appropriate course of action.
   - Support your answers with reference to ethics and the law.
   - Explain why some actions are not ideal, yet not as bad as others.

Once you have absorbed more ethical and legal concepts, you will be able to flesh out this three-stage model. The great thing about healthcare ethics (and law) specifically in a medical interview setting, is that all the same concepts are utilised. You need to adapt yourself to different situations and make sure you identify the underlying issues (situational analysis). You can then proceed with 'evaluations', 'conclusions' and 'comparative justifications'. This process is similar to how you practice medicine as a junior doctor – the justification for asking you all of these difficult questions in the first place.

Basic Legal Concepts and Legislature

Below is a selection of important and common health-related laws. You should familiarise yourself with these topics and think about the ethical principles that might also be involved. In medical interviews you will get marks for identifying legal issues and referring to case-law, specific legislation (like white papers) and defined legal concepts (like competence). You will gain further marks by applying this knowledge to the situation at hand. You are likely to lose marks for irrelevant or superfluous information. This is because the ultimate aim of ethico-legal questions is to make you decide upon a course of action, not to give them a history lesson.

Competence, Capacity, Informed Consent and the Mental Capacity Act

In keeping with the ethical principle of autonomy, patients are generally required to give consent for specific medical and surgical procedures. Essentially, doctors suggest a treatment that they believe is in their best interests and will result in a relative reduction in harm (i.e. the potential harm of the procedure is less than the perceived harm of not having the treatment).

Consent is a formal process with a legal basis. It can be written, verbal or implied depending upon the type of procedure and relative risk. Minor procedures such as taking blood and inserting cannulae, usually come under implied consent. These should still be explained fully, and ideally a patient should provide verbal consent at least. It is best practice to get consent wherever possible and to detail all action taken in the patients notes. For more invasive treatments such as surgery and a medical procedure that could lead to pain or disability (like a lumbar spine puncture), a patient should fill out a consent form.

Consent has some other important aspects that should also be appreciated. Consent can only be taken from a person who is legally competent to make decisions specific to the proposed procedure. Competence is based upon a patient's capacity as defined by the Mental Capacity Act 2005 and their age. The law is also slightly different for children under

18 years. The following describes the key features of consent, competence and capacity:

- Consent is voluntary and can be withdrawn at any time (autonomy).
- Adult patients (18+) are by default legally competent to consent to (or refuse) treatment.
- They must however have the mental capacity to make these decisions.
- Assessment of capacity is defined by the Mental Capacity Act 2005 and requires doctors to ensure that patients key capacity criteria.

Being deemed to have full capacity requires all of the following criteria to be met:

- The patient must be able to understand information relevant to the decision.
- The patient must be able to retain this information.
- The patient must be able to weigh up the risks, benefits and alternatives.
- The patient must be able to communicate their reasoned decision
- The above criteria are for specific treatments, issues or actions. Each new intervention requires a new assessment of capacity. Capacity can also fluctuate in some individuals (with dementia or delirium for example), so this assessment is may need to be repeated or done at another time, when the patient may be more likely to have capacity – it the situation is not time critical.

Children 16-17 are also legally competent by default but only with regards to the following:

- They can consent to treatment, and are legally competent by default, to do this.
- They can technically refuse treatment but, this can be overridden by parents and doctors or a law court.

The Care Quality Commission (CQC) has some great simplified summaries of consent in under 18s. These are linked in the further reading section of this book.

In the absence of capacity, doctors can act in the best interests of a patient. Some patients provide advanced statements/directives detailing their views on specific treatments, which were written at a time when they had capacity. These can be adhered to by doctors when making treatment decisions. Similarly, patients can appoint an individual with lasting or enduring power of attorney, who is legally authorised to make decisions on their behalf. Lastly if a patient has fluctuating or variable capacity, they need to be approached with caution. Capacity assessment is specific to certain actions or treatments. Although a patient may not have capacity for some procedures, they may have capacity for others. Likewise, if somebody's capacity returns (e.g. an elderly patient who recovers from delirium) or they

withdraw their consent, this must be acknowledged and their capacity must formally be reassessed – and their new decision respected if they have full capacity.

Under 16's, Gillick Competence and the Fraser Guidelines

Consent in children can be a bit of a grey area, but fortunately there was a landmark case that led to the formulation of the Fraser guidelines, to determine competence and capacity in under 16's. These guidelines are restricted though. Children under 16 can only provide consent for minor or relatively low risk treatments. They cannot refuse potentially life-saving treatments, if they are deemed to be in their best interests. For example, if a child did not want to have an emergency appendicectomy; their autonomy could be overruled by the doctor and their parents, to provide a potentially life-saving procedure.

Gillick Versus West Norfolk and Wisbech Area Health Authority

Victoria Gillick was the mother of a girl, under-16, who received contraception services from her doctor. Mrs. Gillick also happened to be an active campaigner against such services, maintaining that it encouraged underage children to engage in sexual intercourse. She therefore decided to sue the health authority to prevent such services being available to others. The health authority's standpoint was that if a child is engaging in (potentially harmful) sexual activities, they are entitled to contraceptive services as a matter of safety. They maintained that parents' autonomy should be overruled in preference of the child's best interests, and that it was also not appropriate to breech confidentiality and inform their parents, as this could potentially harm the child's mental health and wellbeing.

The final ruling was in favour of the health authority but there was an acceptance that individual variation means that guidelines are necessary for doctors. The Fraser guidelines were produced to assess whether contraceptive services are indicated for a patient under 16. These are listed below:

- The child can understand the contraceptive advice.
- They cannot be persuaded to inform their parents that they want contraceptive services.
- They are likely to continue having unprotected sex.
- They may come to harm if contraceptive services are not provided.
- It is in the child's best interest, psychologically and physically, to provide contraception whilst not informing their parents.

The Fraser Guidelines are specific to the assessing a child's competence to consent to sexual health advice, treatment and termination of pregnancy. Inherent to the application of these guidelines is also the issue of safeguarding a child who is potentially being abused. If there is any concern of abuse then this case would need further investigation. It would be highly advisable to seek senior input and that of the MPS or MDU, alongside reviewing other professional guidelines and independent legal advice. Another caveat to applying the Fraser Guidelines and assessing for Gillick competence, is that children under the age of 13 are not deemed competent to consent to any form of sexual activity. In this eventuality, evidence of sexual activity would always be deemed as abuse and safeguarding protocols should be instigated.

It is important to note that while the Fraser Guidelines have a more limited remit, Gillick Competence has also been applied to other low risk procedures that under 16's can consent to. This is only really necessary if there is a disagreement between the parents and the child, or if the child does not want to involve their parents. In such a case the doctor's assessment of best interest is usually combined with an interpretation of the above guidelines, but individual cases have individual quirks. These situations are definitely worth discussing with the MDU or MPS. Again, the CQC has published a useful online document to help you navigate the application of the Fraser Guidelines and the assessment of Gillick competence (see further reading section).

Important Legislation

Human Rights Act 1998

This act became law in October 2000. It essentially accommodates all the sections of the European Convention on Human Rights and brings them into UK law. This act applies to all public bodies from hospitals and GP surgeries to schools, government organisations and the courts. Below is a list of the major rights:

- Right to life
- Prohibition of torture
- Prohibition of slavery and forced labour
- Right to liberty and security
- Right to a fair trial
- No punishment without law
- Right to respect for private and family life
- Freedom of thought, conscience and religion
- Freedom of expression
- Freedom of assembly and association
- Right to marry
- Prohibition of discrimination
- Restrictions on political activity of aliens
- Prohibition of abuse of rights
- Limitation on use of restrictions on rights
- Protection of property
- Right to education
- Right to free elections

It is important to note however, that there can be 'conflicts of interests', where the rights of individuals can oppose each other. For example, the right to 'freedom of expression' in a situation where one person's expressed views may cause harm or offense to another individual. In these situations, a court would determine the legal limitation of the rights above. Generally speaking, the decision would aim to prevent harm whilst supporting the other ethical principles, all in keeping with the above legislature.

Data protection Act 1998

This law concerns the possession and treatment of personal data. This could be anything from phone numbers to detailed medical records. All data must be kept securely and be processed 'fairly and lawfully' (justice). Essentially organisations are only allowed to keep information on individuals for a very limited number of reasons. The major reasons are listed below:

Data can be processed:

- For the provision of a service agreed to by the data subject.

- As part of a contractually agreed process entered into by the data subject.

- In order to uphold the law and for other legal processes – with or without consent.
- To provide services essential to the data subject such as medical care.

- To provide services essential to the data subject where consent is not possible – for example unconscious patients.
- To provide essential services to other parties where consent from the data subject has been unreasonably withheld – for example criminal investigations.

There is more detail on the legislation.gov.uk website but it is quite detailed. Your job is to analyse this subject in terms of the four ethical principles plus reference to the Data Protection Act 1998. The following questions must therefore be asked:

- Does the patient want their data to be processed? *Autonomy*
- Is it in the patient's best interests for their data to be processed? *Beneficence*
- Does processing the patient's data prevent, reduce or avert harm? *Non-maleficence*
- Are there supporting reasons in the Data Protection Act legislation to support data processing? *Justice & Law*

Freedom of Information Act 2000

This act was developed under the last Labour Government. It basically enables individuals to access publicly held information. You can think of it as the opposite to the Data Protection Act 1998, which relates to information processing and storage. Any individual can make a freedom of information (FOI) request of the following bodies:

- Public authorities such as government departments
- Hybrid public authorities such as large organisations like the BBC
- Publicly owned companies

In theory, any information that might be, 'in the public interest' can be provided as part of an FOI request. In reality, there are several exemptions, and for mostly obvious reasons. These include the following:

- Information relating to security issues
- If the information is readily available elsewhere
- Sealed court, parliamentary or House of Lords documents
- Information provided in confidence, or when other laws prevent its divulgence.

If the data requested is not in one of the above exemption categories, it might still be subjected to a 'public interest test'; it has to be proven that revealing the data is both in the public's (best) interests and that its revelation would not cause any harm to individuals and organisations.

Abortion Act 1967 & Human Fertilisation and Embryology (HFE) Act 1990

This is a really important subject as it regularly comes up in interview questions. This is because there are many interconnected ethical and legal concepts here including:

- Right to life,
- Potential for bodily harm,
- Consideration of best interests of the mother and a potential baby,
- Freedom of choice and expression and
- Autonomy over one's own body.

You need to know the basics of these laws and that they are slightly different in Northern Ireland (NI) and mainland UK:

- The Abortion Act came into force in April 1968.
- It legalised abortion in the UK (excluding NI) up to 28 weeks of gestation.
- The HFE act reduced this to 24 weeks.
- Further consultation was held to reduce this in 2008 but the law remained unchanged.

In England, Wales and Scotland, pregnancy can be terminated up to 24 weeks to 'prevent grave permanent injury to the mental or physical health of the pregnant woman'; or where there is 'substantial risk of physical or mental abnormalities' that would lead to the child being 'seriously handicapped'. The risk of harm to the mother or the potential baby is deemed greater than the harm caused by the termination itself. In practice, termination of pregnancy must adhere to the following points:

- Termination must be achieved by a 'registered medical practitioner'.
- Termination must be achieved in a registered establishment for such a procedure.
- The 'professional opinions of two registered medical practitioners' are required for termination of pregnancy.
- There must be documented adherence to the three previous points above.

- Any failure to demonstrate these actions could leave doctors open to criminal prosecution under the Offences Against the Person Act 1861 (England and Wales).

With respect to 'right to life' and the Human Rights Act, embryos and fetuses are not considered to be legal individuals. In practice, until a baby is born it has no right to life under UK law. Related to this, abortions have been performed in the UK (except NI) up to full term (full gestation). In circumstances where it can be proved that harm to the mother is apparent or would result from carrying a baby to term, there are legal grounds for an abortion under the Abortion Act 1967. By default, a mother has a right to life as an established human being, the fetus does not. Notwithstanding this, the above points must still be adhered to in order for a termination of pregnancy to be deemed legal.

In NI abortion is theoretically legal. This is provided for by the 1945 Criminal Justice act. In practice however it is essentially illegal in every circumstance (under the Offences Against the Person Act 1861), except when it can be proved that the woman is in imminent danger of death. This is a difficult decision to make for healthcare staff and abortion remains a highly contentious issue in NI. There is a legal precedent for women travelling to England for abortions without being prosecuted, but this also is a grey area and cannot (yet) be provided by the NHS. Following the referendum on the repeal of abortion laws in the Republic of Ireland, NI will soon be alone in its implementation of relatively strict abortion regulation. In fact, there is already a politically will to see change in the province, but this requires the due processes of democracy. In reality, there are many political factions who are deeply opposed to any such change. Watch this space as it could become the next big controversial healthcare topic, perfect for asking about in medical interviews.

Human Tissue Act 2004

This act oversaw the introduction of the Human Tissue Authority. It was introduced in the wake of the Alder Hey organs scandal. Here children's organs were being retained at Alder Hey Children's hospital, without their consent. The Human Tissue Authority now strictly regulates human tissue including donated cadavers to medical schools, for art exhibitions and educational purposes. Anyone in receipt of or who stores human tissue for any reason needs to be registered with and regulated by the Human Tissue Authority. In body donation, the wishes of the individual take legal priority over the family's, especially if there is an advanced directive or will, detailing plans for their body after death.

Interestingly, this act also introduced anonymous organ donation. Previously a living person could only donate an organ to someone with whom they had an emotional or family connection. Finally, the act prohibits the sale of one's organs. There was even a successful conviction in 2007 for a man who attempted to sell his kidney to pay his gambling debts.

Mental Health Act 1983 (amended in 2007)

This act gives doctors, nurses and police the ability to detain patients, depending upon where they are situated at the time. The major points are as follows:

Section 2 – assessment order:
- Mentally ill patients are detained for assessment for up to 28 days.
- Requires two doctors and an approved mental health professional (AMHP), who is normally a social worker but can be another professional with experience or training in mental disorders.
- At least one of the doctors should be section 12 approved (a psychiatrist or GP or other doctor with mental health training).
- Mental Health Act assessment can take place in hospital, in a patient's home or at a police station.

Section 3 – treatment order:

- Mentally ill patients are detained for treatment.
- Lasts for six months but can be reviewed and extended.
- Initiated in the same fashion as Section Two, but requires a diagnosis first.

Section 4 – emergency order:

- One doctor and an AMHP can detain a patient for 72 hours until an appropriate section (2 or 3) can be arranged.
- This often happens outside of hospital.

Section 5(2) – holding of inpatients:

- Any doctor can detain an inpatient for up to 72 hours until an appropriate re-assessment and section can be put in place.
- These patients are occasionally discharged, if there is no indication to section them further.

Section 5(4) – holding of inpatients:

- This is essentially the same as section 5(2) but actioned by a mental health nurse.
- It lasts only six hours, but can be topped up to 72 hours if (any) doctor agrees with the decision – making it a section 5(2).
- It requires review for sectioning or discharge as above.

Section 135 – magistrates order:

- Applied for by an AMHP
- Provides police officers with the legal right to enter a person's home and take them to a place of safety (usually hospital) if they are deemed to have a mental disorder.

Section 136 – police officer's order:

- Same as the above section but from a public place.
- Both 135 and 136 require further review and assessment in hospital.
- If no further sectioning is indicated they can be discharged.

Euthanasia and Physician-assisted Suicide

Euthanasia is a commonly discussed ethical subject. It literally means 'good death' (in Ancient Greek). It is defined as actively ending a person's life in order to reduce their suffering. It can be viewed in terms of autonomy over one's own body and a doctor's perception of suffering not being in their best interests. It is closely linked to 'physician-assisted suicide'. This, as the names suggest, is where death is brought about indirectly by assisting a patient's attempts to end their own life.

Despite recent topical ethical debate, euthanasia and assisted suicide remain as fundamentally legal issues. It is illegal to prematurely end a patient's life for any reason. Any actions that could be seen to adhere to this are punishable under the 'Offences Against the Person Act 1861' (which includes murder, manslaughter and assault etc.) The 'Suicide Act 1961', is used to prosecute any indirect assistance provided to a patient who actively ends their own life. Suicide itself has not been illegal since 1961, but assisting the process in any way is still against the law.

It is **not** illegal to allow a patient to die by natural means, if this is deemed to be in their best interest. For example, removing a patient from life support or not administering life-saving cardiopulmonary resuscitation. This is where ethics takes over in situations where resuscitation is impractical and unlikely to be successful. 'Do not cardiopulmonary resuscitate' or DNACPR forms have been a point of media contention recently, as the decision to make these judgments is purely objective and purely a medical decision (in the patient's best interests). Following recent legal cases, it is now impressed upon doctors that it is good practice to engage with and involve the family in such critical decisions. Additionally, it is considered good practice to involve patients regarding decisions made about their own care. This may not always be a good idea as it can cause distress (i.e. harm) and should be discussed with senior colleagues first. There is also the question as to whether the patient has the capacity to understand their care decisions. As ever all cases and all patients, have their own individual quirks. Thus underscoring both the importance and the dynamic nature of the doctor-patient (and healthcare team) relationship(s).

End-of-life care is an interesting area of medicine. Irrespective of ethical justification (autonomy and best interests), and if a patient has full capacity to competently request it, euthanasia and assisted suicide are universally forbidden under UK law. Previously, there had been discussion as to whether opiate medications provided for analgesia purposes could shorten a dying patient's life; constituting euthanasia and leaving a clinician open to prosecution. The ethical defence for this is the 'Doctrine of Double Effect', stating that one action could have two outcomes – one good (analgaesic effect) and one bad (premature death). Provided that your actions are instigated in order to bring about the 'good' effect, the secondary 'bad' effect is ethically justifiable.

Incidentally, there is little convincing scientific evidence to support the premise that opiate analgaesia precipitates early death in end-of-life care. As such, this is more of an academic topic for discussion than something that is likely to lead to legal ramifications. Some academics have also argued that physicians' fear of prosecution in relation to euthanasia, could lead to reduced use of appropriate pain medication; thereby harming patients, restricting their autonomy (if they ask for analgaesia), and preventing treatment that is arguably in their best interests. In practice, and provided that you follow the appropriate national and local guidelines, you would be unlikely to face any clinical issues here. Notwithstanding this, the Doctrine of Double Effect is a great model to which you can apply ethico-legal reasoning; the big hint being that related questions may pop up in interview settings

Part 3: Applied Ethico-Legal Topics

Below is a selection of common topics that tend to come up at interview. You may also witness some of these issues in your work experience or come across them in the news, or even in your wider reading. This section is designed to show two things: the application of ethical and legal theory, and also that the same issues are recycled in different situations. There really are a very limited number of ethical and legal concepts that are likely to arise at interview; if you can see through the question to the core issues then you should be able to get all of the marks. Just remember to apply the logical process that we talked about earlier in this chapter i.e. **situational analysis, situational evaluation, conclusions and comparative justifications**

For simplicity and ease of understanding, each of the topics below will be dissected according to this model.

1) Topic: Withholding Consent with Capacity

A Jehovah's witness (over 18 years old), is bleeding from a wound after a knife attack. They require a blood transfusion but have declined this. They have full capacity. You document their competent decision and they subsequently become unconscious and go into shock secondary to blood loss. What are the ethico-legal issues and what would you do?

Situational analysis – what are the issues; spell it out to get the marks?

- A legally competent adult has refused a life-saving procedure.
- This was documented clearly prior to them becoming unresponsive.
- The question states that their decision is competent so you can assume an assessment of capacity has taken place.

Situational evaluation – what is good and what is bad?

- Not giving a blood transfusion respects their autonomy (good).
- Not providing treatment is not in their objective best interests as they are likely to face significant harm, including death (bad).
- Formal assessments of capacity and competence have taken place and these have been recorded in the notes (good – there is a clear legal basis for your actions, available for all to see).

Conclusions and comparative justifications – what would you do and why?

- Not transfusing is the best option. It is legally justified (competence/capacity) and ethically justified (respect for autonomy).
- Transfusing would save their life, but would not be legally justified in the presence of a recorded decision to decline this treatment in a competent adult. It also disregards their autonomy and does harm my introducing a foreign substance that they have categorically refused on religious grounds. Transfusion may save the patient's life but may conceivably lead to significant emotional, psychological and spiritual distress, so it is arguably not in their best interests either.
- In order to protect yourself and the patient, you should seek the advice of clinical seniors, a medical defence organisation and consult your trust or local authority guidelines. All actions should be documented with the date, time and your signature, so there is a clear trail for legal investigation of your actions.
- You should also note that serious decision like this are best decided as a healthcare team, in advance of the patients becoming unresponsive. If the situation allows, it would be best practice to convene a multi-disciplinary team (MDT) meeting on the issue and to formulate a detailed management plan.

2) Topic: Cadaveric Organ Donation and NHS Resources

One liver is available and there are two potential recipients: an alcoholic 50-year-old smoker with liver failure secondary to cirrhosis, or a 30-year-old mother of three with liver failure secondary to acquired hepatitis. How would you allocate the liver?

Situational analysis – what are the issues; spell it out to get the marks?

- Two individuals are eligible for a single organ.
- Two individuals both have organ failure and are equally in need of the organ.
- One individual is older and has lifestyle risk factors that could affect the organ's health and function; is the cirrhosis definitely due to excessive alcohol consumption?.
- One individual is younger and has dependents; we don't know how she acquired hepatitis.
- There is no other background information on either individual.

Situational evaluation – what is good and what is bad?

- Providing either individual with the liver would prevent harm, be in their best interests, and respect autonomy if they are requesting the procedure (good).
- Denying either individual the organ could lead to harm including death, it would not be in their best interests and would disregard their autonomy if they had requested the transplant (bad).

Conclusions and comparative justifications – what would you do and why?

- This is a common but difficult question that doesn't really have a definitive answer as you are choosing between human beings living and dying as a result of your actions.
- You could attempt to press for more information but you are unlikely to get it.
- Essentially you should make a choice that causes the most benefit and prevents the most harm.
- Providing the liver to the mother of three would provide stability and income for

her family as well as saving her life.

- This is somewhat or a red herring as you should really be focusing on impact of organ donation on the individual and their quality of life

- Providing the liver to the 50-year-old man would save his life but there is no guarantee that he would stop drinking. This would cause harm to the new liver and he could still die. Again we are assuming that his drinking has caused his previous liver cirrhosis and that he has not been able to provide convincing evidence of rehabilitation – ask for more information before you are forced into any assumption

- If you wanted to get really scientific and clinical, you could look at quality adjusted life years (QALYs) and attempt to determine some object method of assessing the quantitative and qualitative benefit of organ transplantation for each individual. In reality, you are unlikely to have time but at least mentioning that that you have read up in this area may score you marks – provided that you can demonstrate understanding.

- Essentially, your focus should be upon providing the most about of benefit for the longest period of time. This requires you to consider the effectiveness and longevity of transplantation for each individual.

- It would be wise to reserve your decision until the very end of your answer, explaining the potential benefit and drawback of transplantation in each case. You may even find that your ultimate choice is equivocal (equally beneficial either way)

- If you do not commit to a choice however, you have missed the point of this scenario and will not be able to get full marks.

- Do some more reading upon the procedures around organ transplantation and related healthcare issues, such as proposed 'opt-in' schemes.

- Demonstrate broad understand and empathy to score full marks.

- Reiterate the need for senior input and decisions to be made as a team

- Mention working in partnership with the patient and respecting ethical principles

- Refer to the legislation around organ donation (see previous section)

3) Topic: Confidentiality, Data Protection and Freedom of Information

A police officer calls the ward asking you to fax him patient details. He says it is in the public interest as the patient 'may be able to help with an active investigation'. The patient is not a suspect. The patient has already declined to speak to the police. How would you respond?

Situational analysis – what are the issues; spell it out to get the marks?

- A request for confidential information has been made from outside of the trust by a professional who is not involved in the patient's care.
- The patient has already declined to engage with the police and is not legally required to do so – they are not under arrest and have not been charged with anything; as far as we know, they are not a suspect, under caution or even a person of interest.
- The patient's personal data is kept securely on hospital servers and can only be accessed by authorised staff members.
- No formal information request has been made by the police officer.
- Are you sure it even is a police officer who called?

- There is no legal basis or requirement to provide the caller with the information requested.
- There is no further justification provided as to why the information has been requested.

Situational evaluation – what is good and what is bad?

- Providing access to securely stored patient data for reasons other than the provision of healthcare, and to individuals who are not involved in their care, is a breach of the Data Protection Act 1998 (bad).
- The Freedom of Information Act does not apply to private, personal information in this context so the request is without legal basis (bad).
- The police officer has not provided any identification to prove who he/she is, nor have they provided a reasonable justification for his request (bad).

- The healthcare professional can refuse the request and the data can remain on a secure database.

Conclusions and comparative justifications – what would you do and why?

- This case is fairly straightforward. Declining to share confidential information is in keeping with the patient's autonomous decision not to engage with the police. It follows legal guidance from the Data Protection Act and it will not compromise the doctor-patient relationship.
- If the police officer were to apply further pressure, the correct course of action would be to defer to a senior colleague.
- In any case, there is no obligation to comply with the police officer's request; your duty of care is to your patients, colleagues and your trust, it does not extend to police investigations.
- Even if the police arrived in person with identification, you would still not be obliged to share information with them in this particular scenario.
- **Unless** the situation changes; your patient is now part of an active investigation where there in a potential risk to the public, the police have confirmed their identification and a formal request is made from the police for to the NHS. For example, there may be an issue of national security as part of a time-sensitive investigation into potential terrorist activity.
- **Still,** appropriate procedures must be followed and information should almost never be given over the phone, without confirming identification, without senior consultation, and when the patient has declined for this to happen.

4)   Topic: Euthanasia and Assisted Suicide

A terminally ill adult patient with cancer asks you to help him to die; how would you respond? He has full capacity and you know that he is suffering with constant pain. What are the ethical and legal issues? He says that if you cannot permanently end his suffering, you could at least double his dose of strong opiate medication so that he cannot feel the pain. Are there any issues with providing strong opiates to dying patients?

Situational analysis – what are the issues; spell it out to get the marks?

- A legally competent individual wishes to die (autonomy, capacity?).
- He has requested the assistance of you, his physician (autonomy).
- You know he is suffering and that death would bring an end to this suffering (non-maleficence and best interests).
- Suicide is legal but it is illegal to (directly or indirectly) facilitate this – i.e. physician-assisted suicide.
- Actively ending a patient's life is euthanasia and this is also illegal.
- Strong opiate medication would reduce the patient's pain but could theoretically shorten their life (beneficence).

Situational evaluation – what is good and what is bad?

- Leaving the patient to suffer perpetuates harm, disregards their autonomy and is not in their best interests (bad).
- Providing stronger opiate analgaesia would address this issue (good).
- Scientific evidence to prove the life-shortening effect of opiates is minimal and delaying pain relief would perpetuate harm (bad).
- You would be ethically protected by the doctrine of double effect provided that your intention was pain relief and not to hasten death (good).
- Death would be a permanent end to the patient's suffering (good) but there is an absolute legal line that cannot be crossed (bad).
- Death by euthanasia or assisted suicide could also constitute harm and would certainly lead to harm to you as a doctor, by way of prosecution and incarceration (bad).

Conclusions and comparative justifications – what would you do and why?

- In a case such as this, there is clear legal guidance from the Offences Against the Person Act and the Suicide Act. These state actions that are not permissible.

- Providing strong opiate analgaesia is entirely justifiable, in keeping with guidelines.

- In practice, you could arrange an analgaesia review with the pain management team

- You must not neglect to mention the doctor-patient relationship and how you must still empathise with your patient to provide the best quality of care

- Explaining why you cannot provide a definite end to the patient's suffering may be indicated as part your educational role as a doctor – it is important to set the parameters of your working relationship

- Sometimes just listening is important, even though it is not what they asked for, it may still help and provides a human connection that clearly demonstrates you have the ability to empathise.

- You must state clearly that you know what the law prohibits; what you would and would not be prepared to do.

- It is always worth falling back on seeking senior advice and discussing the case with the MDT

- You may also wish to enquire about protective factors such as family and whether the patient requires any other professional review, such as a solicitors to set their affairs in order before they die.

- It would be easy in this scenario just to say what you cannot do. Thinking outside the box however and putting yourself in this patients shoes, will really showcase your potential to be an innovative and compassionate healthcare professional.

- Finally, all actions and discussions with the patient should be documented in the notes and you should involve senior colleagues early.

- Guidance can be sought from medical defence organisations.

- This patient may benefit from psychological, psychiatric or counselling services.

- Palliative care teams are specifically equipped to deal with cases such as this – read up on palliative care before you get to the interview; death and dying are commonplace in hospital and in interviews!

5) Topic: Abortion

A 21-year-old woman is 20 weeks pregnant as the result of rape and says she cannot face the shame of giving birth to the child and is feeling suicidal. She has full capacity and the baby was physiologically normal at the last scan. What services are available to her and what laws govern your actions? How do the rights of the mother compare to the rights of the fetus at 20 weeks? Lastly, what would be different if this case were in Northern Ireland?

Situational analysis – what are the issues; spell it out to get the marks?

- This case concerns termination of pregnancy in a competent adult (autonomy and capacity).
- There is a question as to whether this lady's psychological health may be impacted by the birth, and even whether her life would be in danger if she is not permitted a termination (non-maleficence).
- Therefore, a termination could prevent harm (best interests).
- Legally, an abortion could be performed in the UK (excluding NI) if carrying a baby to term could feasibly cause significant and permanent harm to the mother (Abortion Act 1967).
- She is also less than 24 weeks of gestation (the abortion time limit was lowered to 24 weeks under the Human Fertilisation and Embryology Act).
- Legally a fetus has no rights and is not considered a human being until it is born. The fact that the fetus is healthy does not change this.
- The mother is an established life with a right to life under the Human Rights Act.
- Abortion is a contentious issue in NI. It is technically legal in circumstances where the mother's life is at risk or where the fetus is non-viable, or would be at risk of significant deformities (Criminal Justice Act 1945). There is also no legal provision (yet) for the termination of a healthy fetus conceived as a product of rape.
- The law here is (perhaps counterintuitively) somewhat open to interpretation and doctors who precipitate an abortion can still technically be prosecuted under the Offences Against the Person Act 1861, underscoring the importance of clear documentation

Situational evaluation – what is good and what is bad?

- Performing the abortion would respect the mother's autonomy, reduce the harm caused by her shame and be in her best interests as it could prevent her from taking her own life or suffering further emotional distress (good).
- In the UK (excluding NI), this abortion arguably has legal justification and could be performed on the NHS (good).
- Not providing an abortion would preserve the fetus but at the expense of the mother's wellbeing. There is also no legal justification for advocating the rights of the fetus in preference of the woman, in this scenario (bad).
- An abortion in NI would be difficult to justify legally, could lead to the precipitating doctor's prosecution; and the woman would likely have to pay for a private procedure in the mainland United Kingdom.

Conclusions and comparative justifications – what would you do and why?

- Assuming that this case arose in the mainland UK, and there was a consensus between two medical professionals that it was indicated, it could be performed with legal and ethical justifications.
- The current and potential harm, respect for the woman's autonomy and acting in her best interests, all favour a termination of pregnancy.
- Cleary it would not be in the best interests of the fetus not to exist, but legally speaking it does not have status as an established human being.
- Alternatively, if it were deemed that carrying her baby to term would not have any lasting or significant health effects upon the woman, there would be no ethical or legal justification for this abortion. This is because the fetus is healthy and there is no reason why, in theory, this pregnancy could not lead to a healthy baby.

6) Topic: Underage Competence, Capacity and Confidentiality

A 14-year-old girl requests contraception at your GP practice and pleads with you not to tell her mum. How would you respond, what legal basis is there for your actions and what are the ethical issues? Who would you turn to for advice and how would you respond to the child's mother (who is also your patient), when she enquires about her daughter's visit?

Situational analysis – what are the issues; spell it out to get the marks?

- This case involves an underage child who is not legally competent by default.
- She requires an independent assessment of capacity, specific to the issues concerning contraception.
- The doctor should also take a detailed history as sexual intercourse under age 16 is beneath the legal age of consent; she could be in an abusive situation.
- If she is currently engaging in unprotected sex she is at significant risk of harm via sexually transmitted infections (STIs) or unwanted pregnancy.
- This consultation is also an opportunity to educate her about the risks of unprotected sex and to encourage her to wait until she is able to consent legally.
- N.B. if this child were under 13 there would be a requirement to inform social services and or the police as this is by default abuse and statutory rape (if not just rape).
- Aged over 13 and under 16, she is below the age of consent but the risk may be relative. For example, if her and her partner were both consenting 14-year-olds, although technically illegal there would be little prospect of a legal investigation (although the individuals being the same age, clearly does not preclude abuse – every case is different and requires independent assessment.

Situational evaluation – what is good and what is bad?

- If she continues to have unprotected sex she could become pregnant or contract an STI (bad).
- If the doctor does not educate her, dissuade her from her activities or provide contraception, the same outcomes could result (bad).
- If the doctor informs her mother of the consultation, this could be an unnecessary breach of confidentiality that could cause significant harm to the child and her relationship with her mother (bad).
- Providing her with contraception or convincing her to wait until she is 16 are both likely to reduced potential harm (good).
- Convincing her to discuss things with her mother may provide her with additional emotional support at a difficult time (good).
- Alerting the appropriate services if she is demonstrating signs or symptoms of abuse would reduce current and future harm (good).

Conclusions and comparative justifications – what would you do and why?

- If this child demonstrates sufficient maturity to understand, retain, and process the information given and yet cannot be dissuaded from engaging in sexual intercourse, she could be deemed to be Gillick competent. Assessment for this (in this situation) is based upon the Fraser Guidelines.
- These legal guidelines also suggest not sharing information with a child's parent if it might cause them significant distress and lead to further high-risk behaviour.
- Essentially, it is the doctor's job to reduce harm by providing education and counselling at the very least, and contraceptive services if they feel these are necessary.
- This course of action would be in the child's best interests and also support her autonomous decisions (if she is Gillick competent).
- If she is not Gillick competent and over 13, the doctor could alert social services and the police. He could also inform her parents or legal guardians.
- This is where things start to get a little tricky, so early input from clinical seniors and medical defence organisations, is a must.

- It would also be essential to have a female chaperone in the room if any examination needed to be carried out where abuse was suspected.
- Again all conversation and management plans should be clearly documented.
- The fact her mother is also your patient should not influence the standard and quality of care that you provide to her daughter; you would follow the same legal and professional guidelines (and safeguarding protocols if necessary).

7)   Topic: Autonomy and Human Tissue

A dying elderly man has full capacity and would like to leave his body to medical science. His family want to have a traditional open-coffin burial and are not happy with his decision. They have urged you (as his GP) to make him change his mind. The family members who approached you are also your patients. Discuss the ethical and legal issues.

Situational analysis – what are the issues; spell it out to get the marks?

- An individual with full capacity has made an autonomous decision that is in keeping with the law.
- The Human Tissue Act allows the donation of human tissue to institutions that have appropriate licenses and are regulated by the Human Tissue Authority.
- A patient's family has asked a doctor to intervene in their autonomous decision.

Situational evaluation – what is good and what is bad?

- Allowing the body donation to take place would be both legal and would respect autonomy (good).
- Siding with the family and attempting to persuade the patient not to donate their body would be disregarding an autonomous decision from an individual with full capacity (bad).

Conclusions and comparative justifications – what would you do and why?

- In this situation, it would be a good idea to encourage the patient and his family to discuss the issue together. If they can agree together on a course of action, then there is no need for any involvement from their GP.
- If the family refuses to accept the patient's decision, then you should inform them that his decision is competent and that he is legally entitled to donate his body to medical science.
- In keeping with doctor-patient confidentiality, you are not actually required to discuss anything with the family. In this situation they are also your patients, so you would have to counsel them.
- As ever you should seek senior and appropriate legal advice as soon as possible
- Document all discussion for later reference.

8)   Topic: Mental Health Act

A suicidal patient is attempting to leave the ward and threatening to jump off a bridge. What are the issues and what would you do? What specific legislature would you use to govern your actions? Who would you consult for advice in this scenario?

Situational analysis – what are the issues; spell it out to get the marks

- A suicidal patient is currently on the ward but threatening to leave and commit suicide. This would clearly be harmful and not be in their best interests.
- There is legislation (The Mental Health Act) to legally support holding a patient on a ward.
- Section 5(2) can be used by a doctor to detain a patient for further assessment (Section 2) or treatment (under Section 3).

Situational evaluation – what is good and what is bad?

- Allowing the patient to leave may or may not lead to further harm (bad).
- Keeping the patient in the hospital is against their wishes and they may even

have capacity (bad).

- Detaining the patient is legally justified, arguably in their best interests and could theoretically prevent harm (good).
- Detaining the patient could mean that they get treatment and are able to overcome their suicidal ideation or otherwise get better (good).

Conclusions and comparative justifications – what would you do and why?

- In this situation is it better to act quickly to reduce harm.
- Detaining the patient temporarily does disregard their autonomy, but this is only for a short while and does little active harm to them.
- The harm that detention could prevent (death) is significantly more.
- Detention on the ward has a legal basis and is in keeping with best interests, non-maleficence and justice.
- It would be irresponsible not to acknowledge the threats of suicide.
- In a 'best case' scenario, the ward doctor should attempt to reason with the patient and encourage them to stay. In the meantime, an on-call psychiatric doctor could be contacted to make a formal assessment and section the patient for further assessment or treatment. Alternatively, they could be discharged from the ward after having been assessed by an expert.
- This case is all about getting the right people involved as soon as possible.
- Acting quickly could also prevent distress and harm that could be caused to other patients and staff.
- If there were a need to restrain or sedate a patient however, this should always be done for the benefit of the patient and to reduce harm to them – not to others. This is a tricky issue and needs senior doctor and nurse (and preferably psychiatric) involvement straight away.

9) Topic: Alternative Medicine Versus Evidence-based Medicine

A 50-year-old celebrity has been diagnosed with an early-stage, treatable cancer. They tell their GP that they have no faith in modern medicine and are going to try homeopathy instead. The GP is concerned that if they delay treatment further, the cancer will become incurable and the patient will die. They have full capacity. What are the ethical issues?

Situational analysis – what are the issues; spell it out to get the marks?

- In this situation, an adult male is refusing treatment.
- They are legally competent by default but they may not have all of the information.
- This is in addition to there being no evidence (yet) that they have capacity.
- Patients saying that they 'have no faith in modern medicine' does not mean that they are fully informed about cancer treatment – they may not be making an informed decision.
- There is almost no scientific evidence basis to support alternative medicines such as homeopathy, but this is a contentious issue.
- A competent adult is within his rights to seek (legal) alternative therapies (provided they have capacity). Some of these are even regulated by the Foods Standards Agency (FSA).

Situational evaluation – what is good and what is bad?

- Agreeing with the patient and allowing him to pursue alternative medicines would respect his autonomy (good).
- It may lead to delayed treatment and ultimately his death however (bad).
- Forcing a competent adult to have life-saving treatment could be abusive (bad).
- We do not know his capacity status (bad)

Conclusions and comparative justifications – what would you do and why?

- First things first – assess his capacity! If it is intact then move on!
- This is a difficult situation as ethically and legally, the patient is justified in his actions even if they were to lead to his death.
- Another issue here is 'informed decision making'.
- The doctor needs to explore this man's concerns about 'modern medicine' and to find out what alternative treatments he is pursuing.
- Through effective counselling this man could be encouraged to see a cancer specialist, where he could get detailed information and make an informed decision from there.
- Remember, with consent (including refusal of consent), a patient can change their mind at any time.
- For this reason, a GP should arrange a follow-up visit after the man has seen a specialist to check what decision he has made.
- This patient could also be given leaflets and directed to NHS cancer services, then given time to absorb this information in their own time.
- Document everything, confer with senior doctors at the practice, do your own research into the therapies he has suggested and contact oncology to see whether he attended his clinic appointment.
- A key feature of general practice is safety netting - essentially you have to ensure there are ways and means for this patient to stay connected with the health service and ultimately get the treatment he needs. Repeat appointments and   maybe even follow-up phone consultations, all keep the communication open and all offer potential avenues for him to change his mind and seek (modern) medical intervention, appropriate for his condition.

10) Topic: An Inappropriate Senior Colleague (common SJT topic)

Your consultant is acting strangely on the ward and nobody else has noticed. There is no smell of alcohol but you have seen him stumble and slur his words. The ward round is about to start and you are concerned for patient safety and also what to do as an FY1 doctor. Discuss the ethical issues and potential actions.

Situational analysis – what are the issues; spell it out to get the marks?

- There is a potential patient safety issue; if the consultant's decision making is inhibited, patients may get suboptimal treatment (or overtly come to harm).
- There is an issue of potential harm being caused to the consultant too – you have no evidence to suggest the cause of the stumbling and slurring.
- As nobody else is aware of the issue, you appear to be the only person who can raise the alarm or investigate further.

Situational evaluation – what is good and what is bad?

- Preventing the ward round from starting or otherwise removing the consultant from the clinical area could prevent patients from coming to harm (good).
- Directly accusing the consultant of drinking or physically forcing him off the ward would be harmful to him, it would certainly put a strain on your professional relationship and could be seen as assault (bad). It also may not work!
- Allowing the ward round to go ahead could lead to poor patient care (bad).
- Delaying the ward round significantly could also lead to poor care as investigations and managements may be delayed, and patients may suffer (bad).

Conclusions and comparative justifications – what would you do and why?

- This is a difficult scenario as multiple factors are in play. Many of these factors appear to be unknowns too.
- In addition to a duty of care to your patients you also have the same duty of care to your colleagues and to the trust. Many students forget this fact

- In this scenario you could discuss your concerns with a senior medical colleague such as a registrar. If they agree that the consultant is behaving oddly then you could approach him together. If he has been drinking, then together you could encourage him to leave the clinical area. This would maintain patient safety and you could continue the ward round with the registrar.

- Another helpful action would be to inform the head of department or line manager so emergency consultant cover could be arranged (and this issue could be dealt with by senior colleagues).

- It would not be in the consultant's best interests to involve other professionals who are not directly involved (such as nurses, other junior doctors or healthcare assistants). This may cause more harm than good.

- If the consultant was causing a significant disturbance on the ward and there were no senior doctors around to support you, the ward sister is technically in charge and should be approached. You could also call security if you felt it necessary to maintain patient safety. These actions would really be a last resort.

- Essentially you would want to 'mediate the harm'. This involves preventing potential harm (to the patients and colleagues), minimizing current harm (perhaps to the consultant) and removing harm if possible.

- Realistically, your initial investigations should involve as few people as possible, to maintain the consultants dignity, privacy and confidentiality. For example, it may turn out that they are diabetic and are suffering from low-blood sugar. The registrar may be aware of this and could advise delaying the ward round by a few minutes until the consultant can eat something. In this case it would be fortunate that you had not called security about the walking patient safety risk in need of immediate evacuation from the ward.

- Fundamentally, you need to think logical and realistically. You then need to act quickly, decisively and safely. Crucially, you should not act alone and you should seek confirmation of your concerns and evidence to substantiate these.

- This scenario is often a test of your ability to work well within a team alongside testing your understanding or you role as a patient-safety champion.

 **Chapter 4: Significant Organisations**

Mentor's Tip

This chapter provides a brief summary of important medical groups and organisations, which you may come across through discussions or in your wider reading. Some of them have already been mentioned in previous chapters. These descriptions are not detailed; rather they starting points for additional wider reading. It is not necessary for you to know about each of these organisations in great detail. It is important however to know of their basic functions, and how they might relate to your work as a junior doctor (and as a medical student preceding this).

The British Medical Association (BMA)

The BMA is a trade union for doctors. They provide services such as contract checks, medico-legal advice and representation when doctors feel that they have been poorly treated by their employers. The BMA also advocates for safe working environments and rates of pay for doctors. They conduct surveys and provide guidance on practical work-related issues. Of late, they have acted as one voice for doctors to conduct contract negotiations and organize (almost unprecedented) strike action. They also provide helpful guidelines on practical and everyday work related issue and educational opportunities for doctors (and medical students).

It is important to note that the are other trade unions for doctors that are now emerging, such as the Hospital Consultants and Specialists Association (HCSA), and the Medical Practitioners Uinion (part of the larger Unite union). The stage and the players may continue to change in terms of doctors regulation, certainly with the consultants contract negotiations looming. It is a good idea to be aware of multiple new organizations that are starting to support doctors on multiple platforms. Besides trade unions, there are multiple representation groups who are active on social media and some who remits are very specific. For example providing crowdfunding to support legal proceedings for doctors who have potentially discriminated against as a result of whistleblowing actions. You will have to do some internet searching to keep abreast of all the happenings in this field.

The General Medical Council (GMC)

The GMC is the regulatory body and sets professional standards for doctors and medical students. They hold the register of medical practitioners and are responsible for investigating serious incidents involving doctors. They also regulate the performance of doctors through the process of appraisal and revalidation. These are usually conducted each year, by reviewing doctors' portfolios to ensure that each doctor has kept their professional skills and knowledge up-to-date.

The GMC does also provide some useful educational resources for medical students and doctors. Their documents, Tomorrow's Doctors and Good Medical Practice (amongst) others are great to read for prospective medical applicants. Essentially these two resources contain all the things that you should be able to do as a qualified doctors. Medical schools actually base their criteria on Tomorrow's Doctors and Good Medical Practice is where practicing doctors can find the professional duties that they are expected to adhere to when treating patients. Fortunately theses resources are also available in highly accessible online forms. Serious applicants to medical school would be strongly advised to review these in advance of the interview and probably before writing the personal statement too.

Nowadays, the GMC do seem to be seen as the medical police. The media has shown them in the light of medical negligence and mistakes in front line services. Indeed, part and parcel of keeping good doctors adherent to professional standards, is actually removing non-adherent professional from clinical practice. You should be aware of the evolving role of the GMC, their subsidiary called the Medical Practitioners Tribunal Service (MPTS) and recent media cases involving decisions that have gone to the high court. Cue the Hadiza Bawa-Garba case.

Medico-legal Defence Organisations

The Medical Defence Union (MDU) and the Medical Protection Society (MPS) are examples of medico-legal defence organisations. They provide legal representation and advice for doctors when things go wrong. They also offer useful education and training resources like courses on medico-legal subjects. Of particular interest perhaps to prospective medical applicants, are the medico-legal case studies that these organisations release. One great way to complete and excellent answer to an ethical interview question, is to make reference to recent and historical cases. You are strongly advised to search the MDU and MPS websites and see what interest cases you can find.

The National Institute for Health and Clinical Excellence (NICE)

NICE is an independent organisation responsible for evaluating research and publishing evidence-based guidance. They also provide advice to individuals, and other institutions such as royal colleges and the government. Although they receive funding from the department of health, they are functionally independent. NICE guidelines are the product of multiple research studies into a treatment, surgery or medication. They might also focus upon a particular condition with multiple treatment options. MICE produces national guidelines, which are often used in conjunction with local trust guidelines. For example antibiotic use in a certain region.

It is a doctor's job is to reconcile multiple guidelines, with their own clinical experience, senior advice, multidisciplinary perspectives and the person whom they are treating. From this, we create differential diagnosis, evolving management plans and (hopefully) improve the health and wellbeing of our patients. NICE guidelines are a great place to look if you wish to read up on a few common conditions and treatments, as part of your medical wider reading. During your research, you may also find organ or system specific guidelines that have been produced my Royal Colleges or other related educational bodies. Our advice is that you pick a few interesting diseases and look for multiple information and management sources. This would be of particular use if you were to be asked to discuss a disease or body system of interest to you, in your medical interview.

Royal Colleges

Royal Colleges and faculties are educational institutions responsible for training doctors and setting exams. They organise training courses, events and sometimes have their own journals and conduct research. Essentialy, Royal Colleges are linked to specific specialties within medicine and surgery. They set the curricula for exams that allow progressing through a training programme, which ends in consultant status. They also monitor continuing professional development in consultants. For junior doctors and medical students, Royal Colleges provide useful career guidance, introductory and revision courses. Fundamentally, they are responsible for recruitment into their specialty so if you are interested in becoming a particular type doctor, you are advised to research the relevant Royal College.

On this note, it might be of benefit to have some idea of your ultimate career plan but be wary of overspecializing (in your mind), before you have even entered medical school. Really you should be focusing upon following your interests and being able to provide some justifications that you have adequately research your chosen career path. At the end of the day, medical school and then Royal Colleges can teach you how to become a neurosurgeon or a radiologists. Your current challenge is to exhibit a realistic and well informed career choice, alongside the potential to excel in medicine.

Department of Health (DH)

The DH is the government body responsible for funding, (and indirectly) organising and improving healthcare services, and the health of the nation. They make decisions based on discussions within government and in parliament, and make suggestions and plans to improve the NHS. Primarily the DH is a funding body and controls the flow of money from tax revenues (via the Treasury) into dedicated subsidiaries and related organisations, such as the Care Quality Commission (CQC), and Health Education England (HEE). Remaining funds are funneled into NHS England and Public Health England, which further distributed funds and allocated specific budget for end users and patient care.

The funding structure of the NHS is complicated. For this reason, you do not need to know it in great detail. A broad overview however is helpful in communicating a reasonable understanding of the environment you are planning to work in. To provide this overview, the King's Fund has freely accessible infographics, which have readily understandable explanations (see further reading section of this book). The next chapter of this book also provides more information on key aspects of NHS structure, which are of use in the interview and while preparing your personal statement.

NHS England

NHS England is a non-departmental commissioning board and part of the DH. It plays a huge role in planning, budget allocations and commissioning services for the NHS in England. It regulates and monitors how funds are spent in England only. Other devolved nations and provinces of the UK receive separate funding from the Treasury.

National Institute for Health Research (NIHR)

The NIHR is the research arm of the NHS and aims to improve the health of the nation through research. They achieve this by providing research funding, facilities and systems for promoting research. They are made up of a network of researchers and produce publications. This is a great organization to look into as part of your medical wider reading. Here you can find topical and up-to-date research that currently affects the delivery of NHS services.

Health Education England (HEE)

This is the regulatory body that oversees the training and development of junior doctors, en route to becoming a consultant. HEE allocates training numbers and authorizes specific posts in specific trusts, as training posts. Trusts are able to separately and independently offer non-training posts. Generally speaking HEE keeps you in training, if you have met the professional standards of the GMC and the educational requirements from your specific Royal College or the Foundation Programme. HEE basically takes on the combined functions of all the post-graduate deaneries, to regulate the number and quality of doctors in training. Given that HEE technically has the power to remove as well as allocate training numbers, there is also a question as to whether HEE is a secondary employer of junior doctors, alongside the trust/hospital within which they work (See whistleblowing and Chris Day case in Chapter Two: Current Healthcare Issues).

 # Chapter 5: NHS Structure

Mentor's Tip

You will not be expected to know the structure of the NHS in intricate detail. Most students make a common mistake in trying to map out the organisation of the entire NHS health system. Instead of viewing it purely from a hierarchical perspective, try to understand the NHS based on its main components:

1. *NHS values,*
2. *Commissioning,*
3. *Service delivery*
4. *Regulation and monitoring.*

These areas are so important that some medical interview processes base questions directly upon them; you can see the value of wider reading in this area then.

NHS Values

In 2011, the NHS constitution was published following lengthy discussions and contributions from patients, staff and the general public. The constitution outlines the core values of the NHS in relation to patients, staff and the wider public. You may even notice some similarities between the NHS values and medical ethics.

There are six core values:

1. Everyone counts,
2. Working together for patients,
3. Improving lives,
4. Respect and dignity,
5. Commitment to quality of care and
6. Compassion.

Commissioning

Funding the NHS is decided by parliament as part of the 'Spending Round' process. The majority of NHS funding comes from general taxation and national insurance contributions. A minor percentage is from patient contributions, such as prescription charges. In 2016-17, the planned budget for the NHS was roughly £122.2 billion. Initially, this money is passed to the Department of Health, who retain a small percentage for their running fees; national NHS bodie, Public Health England (£4.2 billion) and £7.4 billion to arm's length bodies including NHS Improvement, the Care Quality Commission and Health Education England.

The remainder (£105.9 billion in 2017) is allocated to NHS England. Funded directly from here are services that include primary care, offender, military and specialist services. The majority of NHS England's funding (£76.6 billion in 2017) is given to Clinical Commissioning Groups (CCGs), to decide how they wish to spend the money funding local services. These include community services, mental health, hospital services and ambulance services.

The NHS is a constantly evolving beast, and as such most changes are trasitionary following significant health policy change (i.e. the Health and Social Care Act 2012 – read up on this). In 2017 only two thirds of CCGs were independently commissioning primary medical services (community, mental health, hospital and ambulance services). The remaining third work with NHS England to jointly commission services. This is interested as five years into the newly implemented government policy, things are still not quite working as planned. This is perhaps the nature of the beast, given that it employs over 1.2 million people and serves the entire country.

From some perspectives, the NHS is actually very fast paced and innovative. In 2016/17 £5.8 billion in funding was allocated to the Better Care Fund, with the aim of integrating health and social care services. This fund allows for funding collaboration between local authorities (with funding via Public Health England) and CCGs (with funds provided to them by NHS England). This is probably an example of policy makers reacting to the changing demographics in our ageing society; where social care costs and continually increasing. From a preventative viewpoint, investing in social care has the potential to reduce presentations to hospital and also to reduce inpatient duration (if there is a reduced wait for a nursing or residential home placement, for example).

You should not neglect to read widely into social care the costs and significance of these services could ultimately outweigh healthcare in the near future. Perhaps as a nod to this, Jeremy Hunt's title was changed in 2017 to the Secretary of State for Health and Social Care (where it was just 'health' previously). Even more recently in 2018, the government has announced a further £20 billion in funding for the NHS up to 2023/4. This has yet to materialize and appears to be based upon conditions related to Brexit, amongst other things.

When researching the funding structure of the NHS, you must take political statements with a pinch of salt. Real-terms increases in funding always have to take inflation into account, in addition to the changing health of the population. It may be true to say that NHS funding has never been higher, but if we look at the rate of funding increases since 2009/10 and in relation to GDP, you could argue that this is slowing and moving towards a decrease. There is also the question of GDP-proportional health service funding in relation to our neighboring EU countries. This really is a dynamic and topical issue, that you should keep abreast of all the way up to the interview (and beyond). Don't forget to research the Health and Social Care Act while you are at it.

In the past, service providers were paid 'block contracts', which was a set amount of money. However, this was not considered to be a fair system as some populations were larger than others and different regions had different health problems, which needed more or less funding than others. For this reason, the government introduced a system known as 'payment by results'. Service providers are compensated depending on the number of patients having used the service. Roughly a third of commissioning is done this way, with the remainder still using block contracts. Nearly half of the NHS budget is utilised for emergency services, whereas GP, prescriptions and mental health services, each account for roughly 10% of the entire NHS budget.

Service delivery

The way that services are delivered depends upon where the service users are and what services they require. You may have heard of NHS Foundation Trusts or simply NHS Trusts; these are known as 'providers', because they deliver services. The services that these trusts provide fall into 5 main categories:

1. Primary care services, which include GPs, dentists and pharmacists for example.
2. Acute trusts which provide emergency services in secondary care (usually hospitals).
3. Ambulance trusts, which are responsible for paramedic services e.g. 999 calls.
4. Mental health trusts, which provide services to patients with psychiatric and psychological problems, in primary, community and secondary care.
5. Community services e.g. district nurses, walk-in centres & community rehabilitation

You will find some excellent diagram, infographics and explanations on the NHS and King's Fund websites. Try these resources first in your wider reading.

Regulation and monitoring

As part of clinical governance, there are organisations that are responsible for monitoring services and staff within the NHS; using systems like 'appraisal' and 'revalidation'. These organisations evaluate NHS services and staff in a variety of ways:

- Monitor is a financial regulator.
- The National Quality Board works with different organisations to improve quality and agree the 'NHS quality goals'.
- The Trust Development Authority are responsible for evaluating non-foundation trusts in an attempt to help them attain foundation trust status.
- The Care Quality Commission (CQC) are responsible for assessing hospitals, GPs and other services, to ensure that they are providing safe and high quality care. If they feel that standards are below what is expected, they have the authority to issue warnings and penalties.
- The GMC are responsible for conducting appraisals and setting standards and

issuing guidance for doctors.

- Health Education England provide training numbers for specialty doctors
- The King's Fund is an independent charity working to improve health and care in England
- NHS Improvement oversees foundation and NHS trusts

Mentor's Tip

You should read up on each of these organisations and any others that you come across. Again, you should seek to demonstrate broad (not deep) understanding of the NHS; its structure, funding pathways and status as a dynamic and evolving entity that is constantly tackling the many challenges of maintaining the health (and now social wellbeing), of the nation.

In addition to reading about what is happening currently and the key changes of the recent past, you should also start thinking about how the NHS might look in the near future i.e. when you will be practicing as a doctor. This is an emerging favourite topic in medical interviews. It tests your ability to take what you have learned from you wider reading, and extrapolate it into the future – a useful test for a future clinical leader!

Chapter 6: Clinical Governance

What is Clinical Governance?

The most commonly used definition of clinical governance is 'a framework through which NHS organisations are accountable for continually improving the quality of their services and safeguarding high standards of care by creating an environment in which excellence in clinical care will flourish'. *(G Scally and L J Donaldson, 'Clinical governance and the drive for quality improvement in the new NHS in England' BMJ (4 July 1998): 61-65).*

Mentor's Tip

This is a highly complex definition, which you are not required to memorise. Some universities may not expect you to know what clinical governance is. However, it is useful for you to understand the concept, because it demonstrates depth of knowledge. It is also a subject that is closely linked with teaching, research and leadership skills, and can therefore be incorporated into interview answers. If you are going to discuss clinical governance, it is better to have a definition in your own words. Interviewers will be more interested in your level of understanding of this concept, compared with your memory abilities.

This comprehensive definition is actually describing clinical governance as a quality assurance process. This process has three main functions:

1. It ensures high standards of care within the NHS,
2. It evaluates and improves these standards and services, wherever possible,
3. It makes the NHS accountable to the public.

This is achieved through the 'seven pillars of clinical governance', which can easily be remembered using the mnemonic PIRATES:

1. Patient and public involvement (PPI)
2. Information technology usage and maintenance
3. Risk management
4. Audit
5. Teaching, education and training
6. Effectiveness (clinical) and research
7. Staff management

Why is Clinical Governance Important?

Clinical governance is a set of systems and approaches to ensure safe practices, high standards of care and quality improvement, in relation to patients and staff. It began in the 1990s with the Department of Health's NHS reforms, and was adopted by England, Scotland, Wales and Northern Ireland. These principles also apply to private sector organisations. Each department, Trust and organisation is expected to adhere to these principles of clinical governance.

Patient and Public Involvement

This pillar ensures that the NHS is accountable to the public. It also encourages public involvement, so that services can be tailored to suit the public's needs. This is achieved using a variety of activities and at different levels within the NHS organisation. The Patient Advice and Liaison Service (PALS) is an independent service that provides patients with advice and handles complaints. Individual departments may also wish to collect data on their performances from patients, using patient questionnaires and feedback boxes. A similar survey is conducted on a national level by the Healthcare Commission. The data collected from this national survey contributes to hospital rankings. Community groups such as the Local Involvement Networks (LINks), can play a role in advising the types of services that are important to the local population. They will work alongside the Trust

Board of Governors, who are made up of elected community representatives, to advocate for services offered by a particular Trust. These processes empower patients and the public to be more involved in the delivery of services and to appreciate the importance of their own health.

Figure 5: The Seven Pillars of Clinical Governance

This diagram depicts how the different pillars come together to make a better NHS.

Information Technology

Information technology systems are extremely important for recording and confidentially storing patient information. This information should also be recorded in such a way that it can be easily accessed for research audit purposes, at a later date. Maintaining a reliable IT infrastructure ensures the smooth running of clinical and administrative services within the NHS.

Risk Management

Risk management is a principle that promotes safety for patients and staff. This is achieved at various stages and through systems that are implemented within hospitals to keep patients and staff safe. It begins with identifying potential risks in the workplace, using healthcare questionnaires and risk assessments. Then implementing safety protocols, such as disposing safely of sharps, hand washing or prescribing guidelines. It is essential that staff are trained and educated about these protocols too. There must be reporting systems in place, in case of any hazardous events (for example, you may have heard of IR1 forms or a DATIX during your clinical work experience). For this to work correctly, a 'blame-free' culture should be promoted. Mistakes are highlighted so that they can be reviewed and learned from. Depending on the impact of this mistake, it could be investigated and reviewed at a departmental or higher level. Risk management ensures that correct systems are in place for these activities to be conducted.

Clinical Audit

Audit is a type of basic research, but has a specific function: it enables us to efficiently and repeatedly investigate whether a service, practice or treatment in a particular setting, meets the standards which are expected and outlined in the relevant guidelines; these could be NICE guidelines, nationally agreed NHS guidelines or local trust policies, for example. Audit also enables the researcher to suggest improvements, and to investigate whether these improvements have had a positive impact on the service, practice or treatment being studied. This is an essential component of clinical governance, because it evaluates activities taking place at every level of the NHS; from the ward to a national level. Audit ensures that standards are being met throughout the NHS.

Education and Training

Healthcare staff are expected to actively take charge of their own continuing professional development (CPD), as part of lifelong learning. This can be achieved by engaging in research activities, attending conferences, reading journals, completing work-based assessments and exams during training; also by undertaking a yearly formal evaluation called an appraisal. Different aspects of training are overseen by different organisations, depending upon the grade, specialty and profession of the individual healthcare worker. For example, doctors' education begins in medical school; professional standards are set by the GMC, HEE provide specialty training numbers and Royal Colleges set postgraduate educational standards and examinations. It is the individual doctors responsibility to take the guidelines, standards and curricula set by these organisations, and to ensure that they are met or exceeded.

Clinical Effectiveness and Research

This is the supporting pillar for 'evidence-based medicine' (EBM). There is more detail on EBM and research methodology in the next chapter. Doctors are expected to engage in research activities in a variety of ways. This may include conducting research themselves; reading journals to keep their knowledge and skills up-to-date, or discussing research with colleagues at departmental meetings, conferences and journal clubs. Some doctors may even sit on an ethics committee, which reviews research proposals before any practical research can be undertaken. Conducting research is essential to inform best practice; to design clinical policies and protocols. There are organisations that have been set up to undertake, monitor and review this work. These include NICE, National Service Frameworks, Royal Colleges and the GMC. Even the BMA conduct their own research into clinical effectiveness. Conducting research enables the medical community to develop a better understanding of and knowledge base on various subjects. Research informs the design and implementation of new techniques, treatments and investigations, which have the potential to improve patients' health and wellbeing.

Staff Management

In order to run a service effectively and efficiently, it is important that there are enough appropriately trained staff to fulfill these duties. Managers must also have systems to empower staff and encourage CPD. This also includes making staff feel valued and motivated, which will enhance retention. There are clear overlaps here with the core NHS values, listed in Chapter 5. The other obvious overlap in staffing, is into politics and funding. Essentially, managers have a fixed budget and this can only pay for so many doctors (and other healthcare professionals). In reality however, even when there is enough money and enough doctor posts, there might not be enough doctors to fill them; at least from within the UK or the EU.

You may have noticed on your work experience that there are many healthcare professionals from non-EU countries. For most of us, a multicultural NHS is a good thing, after all we have a multicultural society and so this fits logically. Concerns of standardization according to qualifications can be mediated through entrance examinations for doctors i.e. the PLAB exam (you can research this via the internet). There are always a minority of people who seem to be fixated upon issues surrounding immigration and the taking of UK jobs from UK residents. This seems like a logical non sequitur in medicine however, as there are so many unfilled posts in specialties such as psychiatry, accident & emergency, and general practice; it is not for the want of advertising these posts to UK-trained doctors. In short, we need foreign doctors! It seems that the current conservative government has even acknowledged this, despite a well-publicized political manifesto promise to reduce net immigration from hundreds to tens of thousands. At the end of the day, everybody gets sick and everybody needs doctors (alongside all the other healthcare professionals who make up our NHS).

It is certainly an interesting time to be entering the medical profession. Some might argue, it is the best time to become a medical student. We have recently seen significant concern and discontent amongst doctors, resulting in strike action. More recently again however, we are seeing a conservative government seemingly removing immigration caps for doctors; promising to raise more money for NHS services (in part) through increased taxation, and now providing additional funds for social care. You are in a good position because you will be able to see whether much of this comes to fruition, over the next five-10 years, before you become a tax-payer.

Chapter 7: Understanding Research

Why is Research Important to Doctors?

Research helps doctors to make well-informed clinical decisions. The clinical significance of research really came to the forefront of modern medicine, following the EBM working group publication of an article titled, 'Evidence Based Medicine. A new approach to teaching the practice of medicine'. Although doctors have been using studies to inform clinical decisions for many years, this change in teaching practice denounced the use of anecdotal, theoretical and conceptual knowledge, in making critical decisions. EBM shifted decision making to focus onto high-quality evidence (such as randomised controlled trials); in conjunction with important ethical concepts underpinning holistic and patient-centred care (i.e. patient autonomy and multidisciplinary assessment of best interests). In essence, although some clinicians previously practised an EBM-like approach, this is now formalised and widely taught and practised, by all medical professionals.

Figure 6: Evidence-Based Medicine Components

Informed clinical decision-making using EBM requires three main components as illustrated here.

Towards the end of the 20th century, there was a series of important developments, implemented to nurture and encourage the use of EBM. Research needed to be easily accessible and available to clinicians, and therefore the Cochrane Collaboration and medical research search engines like Pubmed, were established. The Cochrane Collaboration is a not-for-profit independent network of researchers, professionals, patients and people interested in health research. This is a global organisation across 120 countries, which aims to evaluate high quality research and publish systematic review articles; in a freely available database known as the Cochrane Library Online.

Similarly, Pubmed is a database of scientific articles, which enables doctors to search for research on a particular subject. In order to ensure that research is of high quality, publishing standards were established; and now all indexed medical articles have to go through a special 'peer-review' process. This is a review system that journals have to undertake, to ensure that they select high quality articles for publication. Research journals get hundreds (if not thousands) of applications a year, so they have to have a an efficient process of identifying which studies are best. Each study is critically appraised by a group of experts (referred to as 'peers'), in that particular field. Based on the peers' recommendations, an article may or may not be published.

EBM-bases systems and organisations were also created to review clinical practice protocols and to keep them updated. These exist at every level, from local to international. One example is the National Institute for Health and Clinical Excellence (NICE), which reviews multiple published articles to inform national guidelines on specific disesases conditions and syndromes; and their respective treatments, interventions and clinical appropriate clinical management approaches.

Many educational resources were also developed to teach and train clinicians and medical students, how to 'critically analyse' research. This allows future doctors to assess raw and processed scientific data, and incorporate it into future practice and quality improvement. Critical appraisal of scientific literature, is taught medical schools and is enshrined in GMC mandated learning outcomes, in Tomorrow's Doctors (Outcomes for graduates – see further reading section), which prescribes the essential competencies of newly qualified doctors.

Quality improvement (which is based up the simplified evidence-based approach in the audit cycle), is also a compulsory component of doctors' postgraduate training. In fact, in the Foundation Training Programme, doctors cannot progress until they have shown evidence of undertaking an audit. In the past, research and quality improvement used to be voluntary but now these have become inherent parts of doctors' everyday practice; alongside their clinical work.

What do you Need to Know About Research?

Given the importance that research plays in medical practice, it is important that prospective medical students appreciate can communicate and understanding of its value and utility. It is not necessary for you to know about research methodologies in great detail, but the following points break scientific research down into some easy to understand principles.

Mentor's Tip

Scientific methodology has a reputation for being intimidating and highly academic. Most of the time this is because educators can overcomplicate things. The purpose of understanding research principles is so that you have the ability to design a research project, which correctly addresses your research question and hypothesis. The hardest part about this chapter is learning the 'research terminology'; words like 'quantitative' and 'qualitative' for example. It is worth spending the time to learn these specific terms and what they mean, so that you can articulate yourself clearly at interview. scientific methodology can easily be simplified into four main categories: type, time, person and setting. If you want to design a study, all that you need to do is to take into account of the 'type, time, person and setting' of your study.

Type: Quantitative vs Qualitative

Most research can be divided into two types: essentially numbers or feelings. Research that measures numbers or categories is referred to as quantitative research, whereas research that studies people's attitudes and emotions is known as qualitative research.

Quantitative research can be further divided into that which collects 'continuous' data (such as numerical values like weight or height) or 'categorical' data, which deals with discrete entities that cannot practically be subdivided. For example, a specific number of children; half a child is no child at all (for obvious biological reasons).Some might argue that quantitative data is better than qualitative data, because there is an assumption that statistics are more reliable. In practice, qualitative research can be just as useful because it can provide answers to questions that quantitative data cannot. For example, you could count the number of unhappy people in a group (quantitative research), but only qualitative research could explain why these people are unhappy; because it studies feelings, perceptions and attitudes.

Most quantitative studies involve counting things (or occurrences) and recording this information on a case record form, or survey. The researcher will then input this information onto a spreadsheet or database, and conduct statistical tests on the resultant datasets. These can range from simple tests such as mean, median and mode to very complex formulas such as multiple-linear regression analysis. Statistical tests are beyond the scope of this chapter, and you will not be expected to have detailed knowledge of them. You may perhaps wish to read up on some basic stats however, if you are applying to classically academic schools, and you have only taken maths to GCSE (for example).

Qualitative research usually involves semi-structured interviews, focus groups, case studies or participant observations, to help answer a research question; usually concerning why people do or do not do certain things. The results are usually recorded as audio or video files, which are then transcribed into a script. Further analysis is commonly conducted using an approach called 'content thematic analysis'. This method enables the researcher to identify 'themes' in the scripts; the researcher identifies recurring topics that are discussed by study participants. Applying a working theory or hypothesis to qualitative data and looking for confirmation of this, is referred to as a deductive approach. Identifying new or originally unsought-for themes and concepts is referred to as inductive qualitative analysis. This often brings about new questions that can lead cyclically back into new hypothesis and further (deductive) qualitative analysis. There are plenty more sub-variations beneath the umbrella of qualitative research, that you can research at your own leisure.

Time: Prospective or Retrospective

Research can either be looking forward (prospective) or backwards (retrospective). For example, if you are interviewing patients and collecting new information that has not been previously stored somewhere, then you are probably doing a prospective study. In contrast, if you are just collecting information from a database or patient records, which were recorded in the past, then you are collecting retrospective data. Theoretically, prospective data is supposed to be more reliable and accurate, because the researcher is collecting it themselves and it is up-to-date. Whereas with retrospective data, you are reliant on the person who recorded the information in the past, which may or may not have been done accurately. In practice however, retrospective datasets and normally more accessible and larger, which leads us on to looking at study samples and populations.

Person: Study Sample and Population

In this section we refer to 'person'. This is just an easy way to remember your study sample and population i.e. the 'people'. Simply put, the 'sample' is who you actually test and the 'population' is the entire group, to whom you attempt to apply your results, findings and conclusions. Ideally, you would test an entire population and your sample would be identical to the population therefore. In reality, populations tend to be too numerous to test in their entirety. In practice therefore, the best sample is one that is as representative of the population as it is possible to be. Essentially we do this by trying to test as many people as we can, and by having a varied sample that is likely to contain a representative cross-section of the populations traits. The obvious caveat here is that different studies test for different variable and traits; there are many other ways in which we can attempt to make our sample representative of the population and to ensure that our results are not a products of procedural artefact, error or bias – more on these later.

Another important point is that the type of population (and sample), actually determines the type of scientific research project:

1) If you are studying one person only, this is referred to as a case-study. Reviewing

multiple cases in a small prospective study is known as a case-series. These are descriptive observational studies, and they take an inductive approach; you may notice interesting things that you think are linked but you have not gone about your research in a formal scientific way i.e. you have no research question or hypothesis to test yet. Case studies and series are a great form of preliminary research that can help you to formulate a hypothesis and pave the way for more detailed (and expensive) research.

2) If you are studying medium to large groups of people (tens, hundreds or even thousands for example), this would normally constitute a cohort or cross-sectional study. The difference being that cohorts are longitudinal studies - they are analysed over a period of time, be it during the past (retrospective) or into the future (prospective). The cross-sectional study could look at exactly the same cohort, but at a specific point in time. Both studies are analytical rather than descriptive (as we would seek to test our hypothesis – a deductive approach – rather than just recording what we see). These studies and are commonly used in medicine and epidemiology (population health), to assess large groups of people who may share similar traits or who are exposed to similar environmental factors. In cohort studies, there is does not need to be an intervention or a control group either. These studies are useful for assessing long term changes in population health or (in the case of a cross-sectional study) taking a broad snapshot of population health. Combining long-term cohort studies and multiple cross-sectional studies, can provide a clearer picture in this field.

3) Adding an artificial intervention (such as a medication) to a study sample or cohort (to measure its effects), is essentially what happens in a drugs trial. In order to determine whether the measured changes in participant characteristics are the result of the drug, a control group is added. This is a separate and parallel sample cohort, which is equally representative of the study population. This is now an interventional or treatment study. It is prospective and conducted under carefully controlled conditions; besides the control group itself, other attempts are made to ensure that the results are reliable and accurate. Namely, making sure both the study and the control group are sufficiently similar in all of their other traits. This is called being comparable at baseline, and it attempts to ensure that factors other than the introduced medication, are not affecting the study findings, as this would invalidate the results.

4) It is possible to take things one step further and to collate and analyse, previously

trials into a meta-analysis. This actually combines multiple samples that are all applicable to the same population. It increases the sample size and theoretically has the potential to provide more reliable results. The tricky thing is making sure that all of these sample groups are comparable (at baseline), and ensuring that the study methodology is similar enough. You can read more about meta-analyses and all other research study types, in Trisha Greenhalghs excellent book: How to Read a Paper (see further reading section)

The way in which a study sample is selected will affect the study's reliability and significance. For example, if the researcher personally selects the research participants; they may choose participants who will give them the results that they want, and purposefully avoid participants that they do not want. This is known as researcher bias. It makes the results of a study less reliable. If the researcher decides to interview and recruit as many patients as possible from a specific clinic, then this is considered to be a 'cross-section' of a study population. This is slightly better than the previous example. The gold standard is 'randomisation'. This is usually achieved using a computer, which randomly selects participants from a given population, thereby eliminating researcher (sampling or selection) bias.

Bias can be minimised further, by making studies 'blind' or 'double-blind'. This usually applies to research that involves testing an intervention to see if it is beneficial, or not. In a blind study, the participant is not informed if they are receiving the experimental intervention (treatment) or an inactive placebo. This helps to eliminate something known as 'the placebo effect', which refers to a phenomenon where a participant will have a positive response to an intervention, simply because they possess an expectation that they will improve as a result of the intervention. For example, in a drug trial where a patient is given a placebo (such as a sugar tablet), the patient thinks that their symptoms have improved because they have taken a tablet and they expect to get better. This can skew results. Therefore if the patient is not told if they are given the placebo or the treatment, this effect is theoretically minimised.

Double-blinded studies go one step further; the researcher and the participant do not know if they have been given a placebo or the actual intervention – minimising researcher/sampling bias too. This works because it is theorised that the researcher might inadvertently give the patient a clue as to whether they are taking an intervention or a placebo, if they themselves know which is being given. A double-blinded study prevents this from happening. A gold standard for a medical drug trial would then be, a randomized, controlled double blind methodology. It is also possible to swap the control and intervention groups part-way through the trial in a 'crossover' approach, further reducing bias and increasing the reliability of results.

Setting: Research Environments

The setting of a research study is important because it can help to answer the research question more appropriately, and also gives an indication of the study's transferability. For example, if a study is conducted in a hospital in India, does this mean that the same results would be obtained in a UK hospital? This may not be the case, because of differing health systems, policies, practices and socio-cultural factors. It is however possible to conduct the same experiment in different yet similar institutions, to create a 'multi-centred' trial. A multi-centred trial is considered to be more robust than a single-centred one, and has the potential to be more applicable to a national or international population, for example. Ideally each centre would conduct its research simultaneously, so that the other centres cannot become aware of any results before their trials are completed. This now adds to our previous gold standard model, to create a:

Simultaneous, multi-centred, randomized, controlled, double-blind, crossover trail.

In theory, the only way this could be bested, is if multiple version of these trails are combined (retrospectively), in a meta-analysis study (as described above).

What Makes Good Research?

It is important for clinicians to be able to differentiate between different research methodologies, and to decide upon which methods are more reliable or perhaps more appropriate for answering a specific research question (or testing a specific hypothesis). In order to do this they need to have an understanding of different research methods (as described above). They may also use tools like the 'hierarchy of evidence' or the 'pyramid of evidence' (Figure 7 below) to help them. The pyramid illustrates the various levels of research, with the weakest or least reliable form of research at the base, and the strongest or most reliable research methodology at the top. In keeping with the pyramid, the weaker studies always tend to be more numerous. They are nearly always cheaper and quicker however, and can always contribute to more detailed research, if they provide convincing preliminary results. On this note, you could also think of the pyramid as an upside-down funnel; any weaker studies that do not produce useful preliminary data can be filtered out. Therefore testing does not progress through to the more expensive and time consuming models, such as a randomized controlled trail.

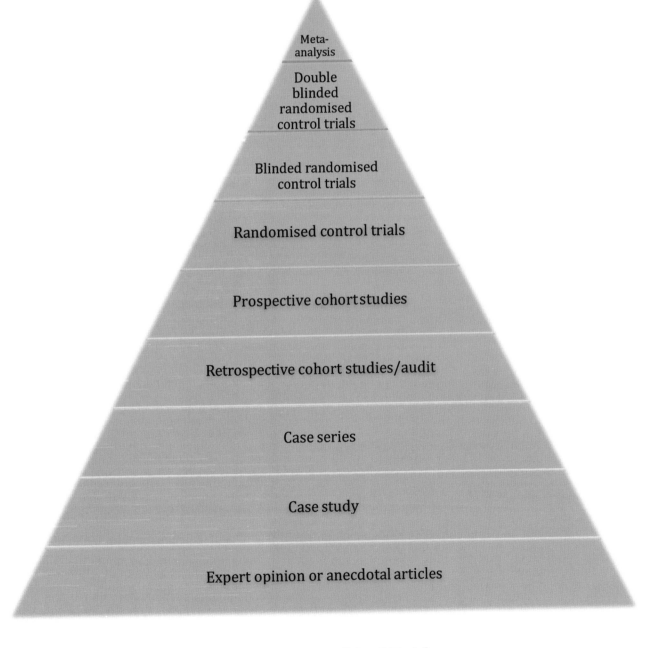

Figure 7: The Pyramid of Evidence

This pyramid depicts the hierarchy of research methods, with the gold standard at the peak and weaker research methods at the base.

Audits

Audit has previously been discussed as one of the pillars of clinical governance. This basic form of research methodology, is designed to quickly evaluate clinical practice and compare it to accepted standards, thus providing a quality assurance (and improvement), process within the clinical governance remit. It enables the researcher to make rapid changes to a system that is not performing to the appropriate standard. Being a cyclical process, audit also allows for the evaluation of newly implemented changes, to provide quick and measurable results in front-line NHS services. There are several stages involved in the audit cycle (Figure 8):

1.   Identifying best practice.
2.   Collecting clinical data to see if this practice is being properly conducted.
3.   Analysing this data and comparing it to the available standard(s).
4.   Suggesting and implementing changes to improve this practice; this might include clarification of local protocols, or better training and/or amendment(s) to clinical practice.
5.   Collecting data again after a period of time, to see if practice has improved within the department. This last stage is also known as 'closing the audit loop'.

Figure 8: The Audit Cycle

This diagram illustrates the different stages of the audit cycle.

The loop is closed when implemented changes are then assessed.

Chapter 8: Transferable Skills

Since medicine is more than just an academic vocation, doctors are expected to have a range of skills that go beyond just the academic. These are often referred to as 'transferable skills'. A transferrable skill is generally one that can be applied to a range of jobs and situations. In medicine, there is a strong emphasis on specific transferrable skills, which were highlighted by the GMC in a document called 'Tomorrow's Doctors' (this is now accessible online as 'Outcomes for graduates' – see further reading section below). These specific skills correlate with desirable attributes of a good doctor, and unsurprisingly therefore appear on application marking criteria for personal statements and interviews. Below is a list of transferrable skills that all doctors must demonstrate. These include the ability to:

- Work within one's competence
- Keep one's knowledge/skills up to date.
- Treat individuals with respect.
- Be honest, polite and act with integrity.
- Listen and communicate effectively.
- Be organised and self-motivated.
- Take initiative.
- Make decisions under pressure.
- Be a good leader and team-player.
- Teach and support the development of one's colleagues.
- Empathise with others.
- Prioritise effectively.
- Cope with stress.
- Ask for help when needed.
- Handle responsibility.
- Be reliable and dependable.
- Reflect and improve.

Many of these skills can be demonstrated through your academic and extra-curricular pursuits, even if the experience is not directly related to medicine. For example, if we take a student who has a part-time job selling shoes in a high street store; they would have to:

Talk to customers – this resembles the following traits of a good doctor:

- *Treats individuals with respect.*
- *Is honest, polite and acts with integrity.*
- *Listens and communicates effectively.*

Promptly refills the displays when stock is low – this resembles the following traits of a good doctor:

- Takes initiative.
- Is organised and prioritises effectively.
- Handles responsibility.

Works quickly during busy periods, like the sales – this resembles the following traits of a good doctor:

- Is a good leader/ team player.
- Copes well with stress.
- Asks for help when needed.
- Makes decisions under pressure

Learns about the different shoe styles and pricing – this resembles the following traits of a good doctor:

- Works within one's competence.
- Keeps one's knowledge/skills up to date.
- Is self-motivated.

Attends work on time – this resembles the following traits of a good doctor:

- Handles responsibility.
- Is reliable and dependable.

Balances work alongside academic studies – this resembles the following traits of a good doctor:

- Prioritises effectively.
- Is organised and self-motivated

Approaches the manager with new ideas to improve sales – this resembles the following traits of a good doctor:

- Takes initiative.
- Teaches and supports the development of one's colleagues.
- Reflects and improves.

These situations and skills are readily transferable to clinical situations where a junior doctor would have to:

- Talk to patients and patients' relatives
- Make sure that all clinical jobs have been completed, and those that are outstanding are chased up.
- Work quickly and efficiently when they are on-call
- Study for exams, read journals and keep one's knowledge up to date.
- Attend work on time.
- Balance work alongside academic studies.
- Approach the supervisor about new ideas for research projects and organise teaching.

Team-Working Skills

Arguably, one of the most important skills is the ability to be a good team-player. Many other skills are developed as a direct result of working within teams; being organised, reliable, supporting colleagues, teaching others and communicating well, for example. It is obvious that in order to effectively lead a team, one must first appreciate what it takes to work well within a team.

What is a Team?

A team is a group of two or more people, who work together towards achieving a common goal. Each member has a clearly defined role, which actively contributes to the overall function of the team. As teams grow in size, a hierarchy may develop in order to provide structure and definition; to organise the team's decision-making and functional activities. For example, a team consisting of two or three members may not require a leader, however a much larger committee often includes leadership and deputy roles.

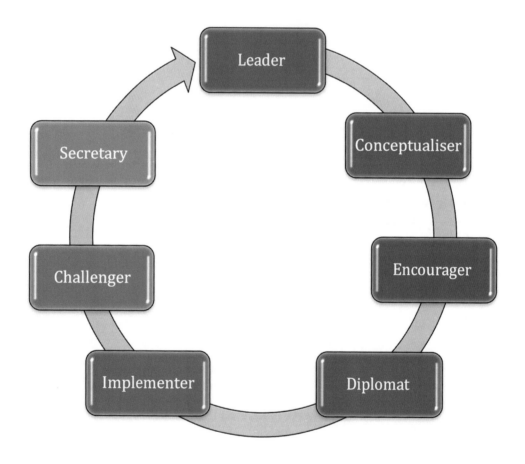

Figure 9: Common Roles Within a Team

This diagram illustrates the different roles within a team. It is possible for one member to occupy more than one role. Which team member(s) are you?

Teams often begin forming with a leader or conceptualiser, before other members are acquired to fulfill the above roles. This does not mean that seven members are needed to create a team; often one individual may inhabit more than one role – particularly in smaller groups. For example, the leader and conceptualiser may be the same person. Let us analyse these roles in more detail:

The Leader

This position provides the team with vision and direction. Often leaders are perceived to be dominant individuals but this is often a fallacy. It is true that confident people gravitate towards this role, but good leaders have the ability to listen and encourage the views of all of the team members. At the same time, they do need to be assertive enough to reign in members who are overpowering others. The leader often exhibits a strong sense of self-motivation and organisation. They are often the most focused members of the group and keep the team on track and working cohesively. In certain situations, a leader may be expected to appoint team roles or delegate jobs. Therefore, a good team leader has the ability to identify the strengths and weaknesses of team members, and to delegate roles and responsibilities based upon these.

Conceptualiser

This role is often referred to as 'the ideas person'. This role requires someone with exceptional problem-solving abilities; in particular the ability to think 'outside the box'. Some people are naturally gifted problem-solvers and easily occupy this role. They also tend to have a creative nature, and can create names, brands, products, slogans and various other innovative solutions. These individuals are often good at seeing the 'big picture', and may be less interested in the practical aspects of implementing an idea. They can be difficult to focus and enthuse once the initial brain-storming stage has passed.

Encourager

There is often a team-member who occupies a supporting and motivational role. It is this member who provides encouragement of ideas, and picks up on colleagues who are stressed or in need of support. The encourager is an empathetic person who is sensitive to feelings and beliefs of others. They often use humour to effectively break up tense situations and to enthuse others. This unique individual is a major contributor in creating a pleasant working environment and reinforces positive team spirit.

Diplomat

The diplomat is someone who is skilled at keeping channels of communication open and considers several points of view, as objectively as possible before coming to a decision. They tend to be the peacekeepers and possess an ability to resolve conflicts within a team. They often exhibit excellent listening and communication skills. They are also flexible and have the ability to develop a good rapport; demonstrating exceptional social skills.

Implementer

The implementer tends to be the most 'grounded' member of the team. They complement the conceptualiser role very well, because they have the ability to see how ideas can be made into a reality. They are drawn to working out the finer details of a project and have good problem-solving and organisational abilities. A good implementer is able to create plans and timelines with realistic deadlines. They are very hardworking and expect others to be the same. They tend to be very calm under pressure and have excellent reflective skills.

Challenger

At first this person may appear antagonistic, but this is not a helpful interpretation of their leadership style. Instead, the challenger's role is to predict potential barriers or problems before they happen. This is crucial, because the challenger can effectively oppose an idea; facilitating the team to make an informed decision about whether the idea will really work practice. These individuals also have excellent problem-solving and analytical abilities, and can often provide alternative methods or ideas themselves. They are essential in preventing teams from making hasty, uninformed and/or poor decisions.

Secretary

The secretary plays an administrative role. This person is essential in recording minutes from meetings; responding to emails and completing all of the essential paperwork, involved in the continuing activities of the group. They have excellent written communication skills; time-management, prioritisation and organisational abilities. They understand the importance of recording information and completing projects to a high standard. They maintain the team's diary and remind others of when deadlines or meetings are coming up.

Positive and Negative Indicators

How do you know that a team is working? There are indicators that can be used to review if a team is working effectively or not. Positive indicators are imperative to help teams work well together; helping team members to identify what specific aspects of teamwork, they are doing well. There are also warning signs for a team that is not working effectively or cohesively. Failures often arise when these signs go unnoticed or are ignored. It is important for a good team player to be familiar with these indicators in order to evaluate how effective a team is. The table below has a list of indicators. If the answer is 'yes' then this is a positive indicator, and if the answer is 'no' it is a negative indicator. Ideally, a good team will be able to answer yes to all of these questions.

The following assessment form has been provided as a guide. You can use the form to learn about your own team working abilities; by asking your peers to complete it for you during group tasks. You can also use it as a reflective tool by completing it for yourself.

Teamwork Indicators Checklist

Indicator	Yes	No
Does the team have clear goals and a vision?		
Are all the team members familiar with these goals?		
Is there a positive, enthusiastic work ethic in the team?		
Do team members feel supported by their colleagues?		
Are deadlines being met?		
Are projects/products/research initiatives being completed to a high standard?		
Does the team generate new ideas and solutions to problems?		
Is there good record keeping of discussions, ideas and evaluations of projects?		
Do team members feel that they have been given roles that play to their strengths?		
Do team members understand and appreciate their roles within the team?		
Do team members feel that they can openly voice their concerns without be discriminated against?		
Have team members had an opportunity to get feedback on their own performance within the group?		
Do team members feel that they get credit (or are appreciated) for the work that they do?		

What is your overall impression of the team?

Rating	Very poor	Poor	Below average	Average	Above average	Very good	Excellent
Points awarded	1	2	3	4	5	6	7

Teamwork Competency Checklist

Assessment Areas	Very poor	Poor	Below average	Average	Above average	Very good	Excellent	Points
Participates willingly								
Actively Influences Events								
Grabs opportunities								
Identifies relevant information								
Introduces new ideas								
Listens to others								
Incorporates everyone's points of view								
Is tactful								
Clearly presents facts and ideas								

Shares new ideas								151
Brings a new point of view								
Helps others								
Encourages all team members								
Understands own role within group								
Completes tasks cohesively and on time								
Provides advice without being patronising								
Makes full use of resources available								
Provides constructive feedback to others								
Reflects on and improves performance								
Does not blame others								

It is also a good idea to reflect on your team-working skills, whenever you have the opportunity to work as part of a team. This will help you to improve and learn from your experiences, as well as contribute to your portfolio of experiences. Here is a reflective template that you can use to do this.

Reflection on Team-working Skills

Provide an objective description of the team-working activity that you were involved in:

What was your role in the group? Did you feel confident about your duties and responsibilities?

Was there anything about this role that you found challenging? How did you overcome these?

Were there any instances where you felt that you worked well with other team members?

Did you face any challenging situations whilst working with others? How did you overcome these?

Did you have an opportunity to participate actively? If so what was your contribution? Did you feel there were times when you could have participated more?

Did you find it easy to express your opinions to others? If not, why did you find it challenging and what could you do to improve next time?

Were you able to provide guidance, focus and new ideas? If so, how did you do this? If not, what prevented you from doing so and what could you do to improve upon this next time?

Overall, which of the above seven roles did you identify with during this experience? Was this a good experience? Are there other ways in which you could have improved?

Leadership

There is no such thing as a perfect leader. People have different leadership styles, which are closely linked to their beliefs and personalities. Therefore, no matter how good a leader you actually are, not everyone will appreciate your particular leadership techniques, and you may get scrutinised by some members of your team. Interestingly, when people criticise our abilities as a leader, this is often more upsetting than other skills such as team-working, communication or teaching, and we tend to take this criticism personally. It is for this reason that when you receive criticism (provided that it is constructive and fair), you must view it as objectively as possible, and as an opportunity for you to improve. Try not to take it personally, because this could inhibit your progress. Your team-mates or 'followers' are the ones who experience your leadership, and are perfectly placed to give you feedback on your leadership style.

What Makes a Good Leader?

Someone who:

- Is a charismatic, likeable person.
- Is a competent individual.
- Is honest and has integrity.

- Treats people politely and with respect.

- Is a good teacher and mentor.

- Is supportive and encouraging of others.

- Is organised and good at project management.

- Considers everyone's ideas and respects their opinions.

- Values team members and provides positive feedback when due.

- Delegates tasks effectively.

- Has vision and goals.

- Is a good problem-solver.

- Takes responsibility for the team.

- Can make decisions under pressure.

- Can persuade and motivate individuals.

- Takes initiative and works hard.

- Can be assertive when needed.

These characteristics appear in the seven roles of a team, as mentioned in the team-working section, which is why it is so important to appreciate and be a good team player; in order to be a good leader.

Charisma

Being charismatic is not necessarily the same as being loud. A lot of it relies on how you present yourself and your body language. Picture a charismatic person in your mind and consider what it is that makes them so. They tend to smile and laugh a lot, appear stress-free and always in a good mood. They make eye contact, vary the tone of their voice when speaking and have a good sense of humour. Sometimes this is also referred to as 'charm', but the really important thing is to be genuine. This means that you must take a genuine interest in the welfare of your team members; you should also be an empathetic and caring person. Use positive body language, which is open, enthusiastic and welcoming;e leaning forward, nodding and actively listening.

Competence

A competent individual is someone who is experienced and has the ability to maintain their colleagues' trust. They are often referred to as the person 'who knows what they are doing'. In order to be experienced at leadership, it is important to put yourself forward and grasp as many leadership opportunities as you can. Very experienced leaders do not wait to be asked; they create opportunities for themselves and know how to build a good team around them. Competence is also closely linked to being reliable and dependable. It is easy enough to make a good first impression, but much harder to maintain that level of trust and faith in colleagues. This is why leaders tend to be the most hardworking members of a team. They must be completely informed on the activities of the group and make decisions that seem reasonable to others.

Honesty, Integrity and Respect

It is not surprising that people often link doctors with leaders, because many of the qualities of a good leader appears in 'Tomorrow's Doctors'; such as honesty, integrity and politeness. Behaving honestly, is not just about telling the truth, but also about maintaining trust and confidentiality. Your team members may confide in you for advice about a situation, and expect that you will maintain that trust. That also means owning up to mistakes that you have made, being open with the team about why you have made certain decisions and having the courage to address conflict within a team. Having integrity also means having sound ethical principles. This involves knowledge of the ethical principles (covered in the ethics chapter). Behaving ethically also demonstrates that you have respect for your colleagues.

Mentoring, Support and Encouragement

A good leader is also a good teacher and will have the patience to talk through problems and encourage the development of skills. All leaders know that if they have a skilled team, then they can accomplish more. Supporting the development of individuals is a good way to make team members feel valued and encouraged

Project Management

A good leader is organised, has excellent time management and delegation skills. They also have the ability to break down talks into easily manageable chunks, by using action plans, master lists and SMART goals. We will discuss these organisational tools later in this chapter.

Decision Making

In order to make a good decision, one needs to be informed. When you are working under pressure this can be extremely challenging; this is when poor decisions are most likely to be made. Lack of time puts pressure on individuals to 'cut-corners', particularly during the planning stages. Encouraging the ideas of your team-members, contributes to making informed decisions. This is why creating a positive working environment is important, because if ideas are shared openly and freely, you are more likely to come to a more informed decision, faster.

Vision and Motivating Others

One thing that can set apart a good leader from a great one is vision. A good leader will have a set of measurable objectives and will work to meet these. A great leader has the ability to visualise success and direct the team towards this. Vision motivation can be a powerful tool; if you can see your end goal then you are more motivated to achieve it, and you can motivate others too. There is more about vision motivation later in this chapter. It is also important to give good feedback when your team members have done something well.

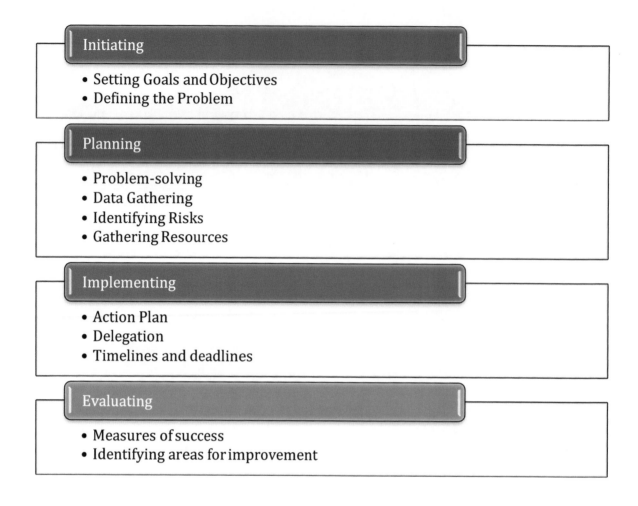

Initiating
- Setting Goals and Objectives
- Defining the Problem

Planning
- Problem-solving
- Data Gathering
- Identifying Risks
- Gathering Resources

Implementing
- Action Plan
- Delegation
- Timelines and deadlines

Evaluating
- Measures of success
- Identifying areas for improvement

Figure 10: Stages of Decision Making

This figure illustrates the stages of decision-making and their components.

Logical decision-making can be demonstrated use this systematic approach.

Persuasiveness

Being persuasive is an art form. Advertisers use persuasive techniques to get what they want, but a good leader uses persuasiveness to get jobs completed; to encourage and motivate their team. A persuasive individual:

- Appreciates his/her audience
- Identifies the most interesting, salient points
- Is well informed
- Is confident
- Knows when to back down and plays a long game.

An unpersuasive individual:

- Cannot empathise with his/her audience, so speaks to everyone in the same way
- Tries to talk about everything and bores the audience
- Is not properly informed and cannot answer questions
- Is shy and unsure
- Is determined to succeed in every argument.

Takes Responsibility and Initiative

Many great leaders lead by example. Leaders are expected to set the standard in a team. It is important to accept responsibility when you take on a leadership role. This is something that most people tend to shy away from, and it can subsequently become very challenging to make decisions. As a student you will often be waiting for instructions from your teachers and parents, on a huge range of tasks. As a leader, you will be expected to take initiative and make decisions about what to do next, without being told.

Assertiveness

It is important to remember that assertiveness does not mean that you have to be dominating, angry or abrupt. However, there may be instances where you have to have the confidence to either stand by your decision or stand up for another member of your team. If there are dominant personalities within a group, it is the leader's responsibility to ensure that all opinions are heard. You may need to use phrases such as "I think that it would be a good idea to give other team members a chance to voice their opinions."

The following assessment form has been provided as a guide. You can use the form to learn about your own leadership abilities, by asking your peers to complete it for you during group tasks. You can also use it as a reflective tool by completing it for yourself.

Leadership Competency Checklist

Assessment Areas	Very poor	Poor	Below average	Average	Above average	Very good	Excellent	Points
Shares a Vision								
Directs group members to achieve that vision								
Clarifies roles								
Delegates according to strengths and weaknesses								
Introduces new ideas								
Listens to others								
Incorporates everyone's points of view								
Is tactful								
Understands the ethical responsibility of being a leader								

Shares new ideas								
Quashes dominant personalities								
Mediates conflict								
Encourages all team members								
Regularly build team spirit								
Taps into people's potential								
Develops individuals								
Maintains integrity and is honest								
Provides constructive feedback to others								
Reflects on and improves performance								

It is also a good idea to reflect on your leadership skills whenever you have the opportunity to lead a team. This will help you to improve and learn from your experiences, as well as contribute to your portfolio. Here is a reflective template that you can use to do this.

Leadership Reflection Template

Please describe a situation where you were a leader of a team:

What did you find easy about this role?

What did you think was the most challenging and why?

How did you overcome these challenges?

What will you do differently next time?

Is there anything that you can do in the meantime to improve your leaderships skills, such as attend a course or do some reading?

Teaching

The word doctor (or doctore in Latin) means teacher, and as such teaching is a huge aspect of the work. This is how doctors and medical students learn and progress in their training. For example, consultants teach their registrars, who teach the junior doctors, who in turn teach medical students and so on. Teaching others also provides you with the opportunity to reinforce your own knowledge, and to develop your teaching style and confidence. Make sure that if you do get a chance to do some teaching, you ask for some feedback on our performance and get some evidence, such as a certificate. This is can be incorporated into your experience portfolio.

There are lots of different ways to get involved in teaching. Here are some ideas:

- Teach your peers – run some chemistry workshops or teach younger students after school or during lunch breaks.
- You can present at conferences, such as Medic Mentor's National Healthcare Weekend.
- Present your project during a lesson or form tutor group meeting.

- Create a podcast, YouTube video or electronic resource about a subject that you have researched.
- Join a society and organise some guest lecture evenings.
- Write articles for the Mentor Magazine.
- Teach abroad – if you get the chance to do some work experience or volunteer for an international charity.

A good teacher is:

- Knowledgeable,
- Caring,
- Flexible,
- Creative,
- A good listener and presenter,
- Dedicated and hardworking,
- Encouraging and motivational,
- Able to give constructive feedback,
- Assertive when needed,
- Confident,
- Fun,
- Organised,
- Trustworthy and
- Honest.

Teaching Methods

Here is a description of a few teaching modalities that you will come across as a student. When you come to do your own teaching, consider which method would work best for your subject and audience. Often, the most effective teachers are able to incorporate a variety of techniques, whilst keeping the subject and content as easy to understand as possible.

Problem-Based Learning (PBL)

Sometimes this is also referred to as 'case method' or 'design thinking'. This also happens to be one of the main modes of teaching medical students, at some UK medical schools. Usually the students are presented with a case, which has a series of questions or problems to solve. It is designed for small groups to brainstorm, dissect into significant topics; to problem-solve and teach one another. This style of teaching enables students to develop transferable skills too, such as teamwork, teaching and communication skills. It suits students who prefer to be more active and involved during lessons.

Traditional Lecture Method

This form of teaching is didactic, and involves a teacher standing at the front of a classroom, presenting all of the information to the students. The teacher will provide 'hand-outs' or revision material from the class. It is sometimes referred to as the 'spoon- feeding approach'. However, it is possible to incorporate some self-learning by providing students with a problem before class, which they need to solve at home. Findings are then discussed during the lecture. This is referred to as the 'flipped classroom' approach, and can make a didactic lecture more interactive.

Gamification

This is a relatively new concept, which is becoming more popular because younger students find it to be a more interesting way to learn. However, it usually involves a lot of preparatory work for the teacher, which makes it more challenging. Students enjoy this method of learning because it involves games, quizzes and sometimes apps. Students are rewarded when they get questions right and it introduces an element of competitiveness, to make the session more interesting. It is also possible to get students to create games for one another; through this process they reinforce their own knowledge of the subject.

Social Media and E-learning Tools

There is an emerging field of online resources, which students use a lot. This can be as simple as Wikipedia, watching a YouTube video or listening to a podcast. Some students have created Facebook pages to generate interest about a health related topic, such as healthy eating or homelessness. Students who are comfortable with information technology can even use website building software to create games, apps and websites to teach other students. The benefit of online technologies is that it is mobile and can be accessed on several devices in any location – wherever the internet is available.

The following assessment form has been provided as a guide. You can use the form to learn about your own teaching abilities by asking your peers to complete it for you during group tasks. You can also use it as a reflective tool by completing it for yourself.

Teaching Competency Checklist

Assessment Areas	Very poor	Poor	Below average	Average	Above average	Very good	Excellent	Points
Speaks clearly								
Adapts teaching style to audience								
Uses a variety of teaching methods								
Knows subject extremely well								
Is friendly and smiles								
Listens to students								
Incorporates everyone's points of view								
Develops skills in others								
Understands the ethical responsibility of being a teacher								

Is creative and engaging								
Uses a variety of resources								
Answers questions effectively								
Encourages participation from all students								
Is approachable								
Taps into people's potential								
Shows compassion								
Maintains integrity and is honest								
Provides constructive feedback to others								
Reflects on and improves performance								

It is also a good idea to reflect on your teaching skills whenever you have the opportunity to teach a group of students. This will help you to improve and learn from your experiences, as well as contribute to your portfolio. Here is a reflective template that you can use to do this.

Teaching Skills Reflective Template

Please describe a situation where you had the opportunity to teach:

What did you find easy about this role?

What did you think was the most challenging and why?

How did you overcome these challenges?

What will you do differently next time?

Is there anything that you can do in the meantime to improve your teaching skills, such as attend a course or do some reading?

Presentation Skills

People will judge you within the first five seconds. To win them over you need to show them that you are smart, enthusiastic and an expert. You have to show them that you have authority, or what actors call 'stage presence'. This is an ability to engage with and command the audience. The best way to become a great presenter is to give lots of presentations. It is just like doing exercise; if you want to run a marathon, then you usually have to train for it!

Qualities of a good presenter:

- A likeable, approachable individual.
- Someone who has a good sense of humour.
- Someone who has taken the time to prepare the presentation.
- Knowledgeable.
- Someone who has the ability to speak at the level of the audience and break down complex information into understandable chunks.
- Someone with an original perspective.

- Someone who makes use of several types of media (including PowerPoint, the whiteboard, and hand-outs etc.).
- Someone who speaks clearly and confidently.
- Someone who looks presentable.
- Someone who is never patronising.

When giving presentations, you need to be flexible enough to appeal to different audiences. You may need to give a presentation to children, or professionals. Depending on your audience, you will be expected to adapt your presentation format and communication style appropriately. It is also important to remember that you will be teaching the audience as well as describing your subject. This is why good presenters also tend to be good teachers.

Interactive task:

When is your next presentation? How are you going to line up a few more this year?

The Scientific Presentation

Most of the presentations that you will be asked to do are subject based, or 'scientific presentations'. If you are doing a scientific presentation then your slides are nearly as important as your talk. Make sure that your presentation is structured. It should have an outline for your talk (such as a contents page slide), and you should have your subject heading on a completely separate slide for impact. If your audience forgets the importance of your subject halfway through, you will have lost their interest and respect. Therefore, it is a good idea to tell them why your talk is important at the beginning and remind them periodically during the presentation.

If you have some aims set out for your talk, make sure that you present the answers and address these aims. Most presentations are only 10-30 minutes long and you do not have the time to go through all of the amazing research that you have done on the subject. Try to keep the content simple and interesting, focusing on the most significant points. Audiences do not like waffle, and can easily switch off if you go into too much detail or off on a tangent. Make your conclusions interesting and relevant to your audience. Ask yourself beforehand, 'why are they going to be interested in my talk?' How will it change the way that they work, think or behave?

It is important to keep your slides simple and limited in number; the general rule is slightly more than 1 slide per minute. For example, if you are giving a talk for 30 minutes, you shoulf have roughly 30-35 slides – not 100! You should try to use other tools such as video clips, whiteboards etc. Whatever type of presentation you are giving, do not forget to be charismatic and vary the tone of your voice and body language. Most importantly, remember to be interesting and persuasive!

The following assessment form has been provided as a guide. You can use the form to learn about your own presentation abilities, by asking your peers to complete it for you during presentations. You can also use it as a reflective tool by completing it for yourself.

Presentation Competency Checklist

Assessment Areas	Very poor	Poor	Below average	Average	Above average	Very good	Excellent	Points
Speaks clearly								
Adapts teaching style to audience								
Uses a variety of teaching methods								
Knows subject extremely well								
Is friendly and smiles								
Listens to audience								
Is charming and charismatic								
Is confident								
Maintains good eye contact								

								177
Is creative and engaging								
Uses a variety of resources								
Answers questions effectively								
Encourages audience participation								
Is approachable								
Varies tone of voice								
Good use of body language								
Has a sense of humour								
Addresses aims and objectives								
Reflects on and improves performance								

It is also a good idea to reflect on your presentation skills whenever you have the opportunity to teach a group of students. This will help you to improve and learn from your experiences, as well as contribute to your portfolio. Here is a reflective template that you can use to do this.

Presentation Skills Reflective Template

Please describe a situation where you had the opportunity to present a topic:

What did you find easy?

What did you think was the most challenging and why?

How did you overcome these challenges?

What will you do differently next time?

Is there anything that you can do in the meantime to improve your presentation skills, such as attend a course or do some reading?

When will you be presenting again?

Organisational Skills

SMART Criteria

We set goals to provide ourselves with focus and motivation. Goal setting can be useful but only if performed correctly. Firstly, check whether your goals meet the **SMART** criteria:

Specific: Avoid being vague. Less specific goals such as, 'I want to become a doctor', will be less achievable than, 'I want to get into at least one medical school'. Goals that are vague and non-specific simply do not provide the motivation and stimulation that you need to see them through.

Measurable: How will you know when your goals have been achieved? For example if your goal is, 'to do well in your exams', how do you know if you have achieved this? Does this mean passing your exams or achieving a certain set of grades? It helps to put a figure on or quantify your achievements.

Attainable: Do not set yourself up to fail. Make sure that your goal is within your reach, in the present and not something that you hope to achieve in 10 years' time. Setting goals that are not readily attainable is the commonest reason why people fail to achieve them in the first place. At the same time, try to be ambitious with your goals. Ensure that you set yourself challenges that you are worthy of. Suddenly, you will realise new ways to succeed, which you had previously overlooked. Setting a goal that is challenging can provide the stimulation you need to achieve it. Alternatively, tasks that are too easy lack the challenge factor, and you may not be motivated enough to complete them.

Realistic: This is similar to attainable but there is a greater emphasis upon your resources. Do you have the time, money and energy to take on this project at the moment? It might be difficult to achieve if you already have a lot on your plate. Can the project be deferred to a later date, when it may be a more realistic endeavour?

Timely: There needs to be a timescale and deadline to this goal. Not only will this motivate you to complete the task, it will help you to distribute your time and resources amongst other on-going challenges and commitments. Without a timescale, the project could go on forever! In essence, this is where you learn to prioritise your goals – a fundamental transferrable skill for doctors, and essential for bringing projects to fruition.

Why do People Fail to Achieve their Goals?

There are several reasons why many goals are not realised. It is important to know why goals fail, so that this does not happen to you. Goals fail because:

- **The will was not there in the first place.** This can be because you were asked to do something that you did not really want to, or it simply was not a priority for you compared to your other tasks.
- **The goal was too easy.** A goal that is too easy is not very exciting and can be easily taken for granted, and therefore never completed.
- **You already believe that you will fail.** Make sure that your goals are set in a positive manner for example, 'I want to conquer Mount Everest' rather than 'I just want to survive climbing Mount Everest'.
- **It is not really a goal, but a vision**. Goals are things that can be accomplished in the near future, rather than things you want to achieve in five or 10 years' time.

The downside of having lots of goals is that when you do not achieve them it can be very disheartening. In this way, they can work against you. If you are aware that goals can have a negative emotional effect, then you instantly become more resilient and more importantly, adaptive. If you have not reached a self-imposed deadline, perhaps it was not entirely realistic – extend it by 10% and keep going. Whatever happens, keep looking forward and creating new goals. These incremental steps are what bring you closer to your attaining your over-arching vision.

Vision Motivation

One of the most powerful tools for productivity is the concept of *vision motivation*. As we have already discussed, motivation is the driver for any goal or project. Therefore, having the ability to harness your motivation at the correct time will enable you to enhance your productivity and take more chances.

Vision motivation is about visualising your success at the end of a project. When planning any type of task, it is always better to start at the very end (or with the desired outcome), and work your way backwards. By using this approach, you will have already completed an action plan – without even realising it!

Vision motivation steps (aka stealth action planning):

1. Write down your idea.

2. Immediately write down why this is important to you? What are the benefits? What do you gain from doing this?

3. Then imagine what it would feel like once you have achieved your goal. Is this feeling enough to motivate you to see this project through? If it is then keep going!

4. When will you need to complete this project? Is there a deadline? Write it down.

5. Now work backwards and break things into small steps, until you reach the beginning.

6. Finally ask yourself if your goals are SMART.

7. Have you planned with the intention to succeed? Are you positive about this project?

8. Get started on each of the steps and stick to your timeline. Forget how big the project is and just take things one step at a time. You will have reached the end without realising – and with much less stress too!

Each time you feel like you are procrastinating, go back and read all of the reasons why you started doing this project in the first place!

Interactive Task

Now take one of your goals and use the process of *vision motivation* described above, to generate your stealth action plan, for this specific goal:

Procrastination

Many hours are wasted each week due to procrastination. Everyone does it. Procrastination is the killer of productivity but there are some steps that you can take to reduce how much you procrastinate.

1. **Admit that you are a procrastinator**. It is often useful to find out exactly how much you procrastinate in a week, by keeping a diary of your activities. You also have to identify which activities you engage in the most, when you are procrastinating. For example, watching TV, spending time with your friends, cooking or baking! Usually these are highly pleasurable tasks with instant gratification. You can see the appeal!

2. **Create a routine to beat procrastination.** Find the action that gets you in the mood to be productive. Some people tidy up their desks, or make lists. Some people listen to music to psych themselves up. Which action gets you in the mood to sit down and do some work?

3.   **Write your motivation, goal or vision on a piece of paper** and put this in a place where you will see it every day. For example, 'I want to get into medical school and become a cardiothoracic surgeon'. You might even have a picture of someone who inspires you (these are often more effective than words). Put this on your desk or somewhere that you spend a lot of time procrastinating, such as the kitchen, living room or next to your Playstation, Nintendo or Xbox!

4.   **Leave things to the last minute.** This contradicts everything that your teachers may have told you throughout your life – but doing things in a hurry can work for you. Often people do not start tasks because they are perfectionists and are subsequently afraid of doing a mediocre job. Whilst this is true of some things such as revising for exams, it is not necessary to do a perfect job in other tasks, such as calling the bank, sending an email or writing the first draft of your essay. Some people make use of the adrenaline rush that they get, when they leave things late, because it makes them more productive.

5.   **Make a *master list* and a *next action list* every morning (more on this later).**

6.   **Work towards an immediate reward.** Instant gratification can be a powerful tool. Give yourself a small task to complete by the end of the day, and you can reward yourself afterwards. This also reinforces positive behaviour!

7.   **Complete your action list by doing the most important job first.** You may have to force yourself to do this, but the most important job is always the one we avoid. Sit down and do this first. It is also possible to procrastinate by doing menial or 'fire-fighting' jobs first, and convincing yourself that you are being productive!

Focus

Now that you have beaten procrastination, it is time to get focused. Multitasking is one of productivity's greatest killers. Do no multitask – fix your mind on one problem, finish it and then move onto the next. Do you remember having to write an essay within a short space of time, and all you did was focus on the essay – because nothing else was more important at that time? Suddenly, after days of not writing anything at all you have written 3000 words in 3 days, just before the deadline! How did you do that? Do you remember how good that felt when you were writing it? You were at your peak level of productivity, and you were able to do this because you had reached your ultimate focusing potential. Imagine if you could do this more often, or if you had the ability to summon this state at will. Your productivity would increase drastically. The key to achieving this is to obliterate multitasking.

There is a difference between being focused and being organised. Highly organised people are not necessarily productive. What you need to learn is to be more productive (which is the end goal of being organised anyway). For example, a personal assistant is a very organised individual, but it is the CEO who is attending the meetings and closing deals. The CEO may not be organised at all, but he/she is very productive.

Group Tasks Together

This is a time-efficient and focused action. Instead of checking your email inbox 20 times a day and replying to emails as soon as they enter your inbox, try to check your email once or twice and reply to all of your emails in one sitting. Texts and phone calls can also become a big distraction, so group these actions together wherever you can.

When you are writing an essay or doing some research – focus solely on the task. Do not drift off onto a link with an interesting or funny hook. This is a distraction and can absorb your time. Shut down all of your unnecessary tabs such as Facebook, email and ASOS!

Finally, you will reach a point where it is impossible to become more organised or productive, without it becoming detrimental to your physical and psychological wellbeing. When this happens, get some extra hands to help you. Alternatively, you could think about expanding your team. This could be as simple as finding a partner to do your research project with, or as extravagant as hiring a virtual assistant. This way your productivity does not need to end with you. As long as your ambition remains and you do not run out of ideas, you can always increase the size of your workforce.

Planning Tools

As well as knowing how to plan projects, you will also need certain resources to help you stay organised. This may include a diary, wall planner or an app on your smartphone. It is also a good idea to invest some time in organising your study environment, because a lot of time can be wasted searching for things. For example, if you have an effective filing system for your notes and coursework, it should not take you more than 30 seconds to find the exact piece of paper that you were looking for. One of the most common tools that people use are lists. These can be for shopping, or large projects. Somehow, breaking tasks into smaller pieces makes the job more manageable and organised. One of these concepts is that of the Master List.

Master Lists

A master list always begins with the date. This is important because, as you cross off items on your list, you will rewrite your master list; over a period of time you may have several master lists. They are useful notes to file away, because it they be used as evidence of time management in your e-portfolio or you may want to look back at them yourself, to trace how long it took you to complete a project. The master list should ideally contain a string of jobs that needs doing, numbered in priority or time order. This could include academic jobs, chores, forms that need to be completed etc. Your master list should be comprehensive, containing every job that you need to do – no matter how large or small.

Here is a
(basic) example:

Master List 2ⁿᵈ March 2019

1) *Get into medical school*

2) *Read chemistry revision guide*

3) *Get Mum a birthday present*

4) *Start a Medic Mentor Student Society*

5) *Win a prize*

6) *Organise work experience*

7) *Get my brown belt in karate*

As you complete tasks on this list, you can cross them off. Psychologically, this is a motivational tool, because as you complete jobs you will literally see the list get smaller and smaller. However, the purpose is not to wait until all of the jobs are completed, to re-write it. Once you have completed roughly 50% of the jobs on the list, you can create a new one. Therefore, you do not have the pressure (and the disappointment) of having to complete all of your jobs. New ideas and jobs are created all of the time, which need to be prioritised over long term goals. During the next few days, you may find that some jobs become redundant; someone else may have completed it or the task may have changed. This is why it is unrealistic to expect to complete every single job, and why some people do not like lists. Your success is demonstrated by how quickly it you can complete a Master list and a continue to adapt to new lists. For example, when you first begin, you may find that you are writing a new list every week. With time, you might have to re-write it every three days. This is a measure that suggests you are completing your jobs more efficiently in a shorter space of time.

Where do People go Wrong?

Sometimes when individuals make such lists, they include large projects; write geography coursework or revise for chemistry exam. This is where the list fails because it can take a very long time before you can actually cross these off your list. For example, you probably will not actually finish revising until the day before your exam, which could be two or three months away. This is why it is important that you have master list and a separate 'next actions' list. A next actions list is composed of small achievable jobs – literally the next step in achieving the tasks on your master list.

Here is an example of a 'next actions' list:

Next Actions List 2nd March 2019

1) *Research medical courses*

2) *Book a course*

3) *Order a medical application guide*

4) *Read chapter 7 of chemistry revision guide*

5) *Speak to Mum about what she wants for her birthday*

6) *Speak to friends at school about starting a Medic Mentor Society*

7) *Do an online search of prizes that I can apply to throughout the year*

8) *Get hospital work experience coordinator's number / email from the internet*

9) *Speak to or email the hospital work experience coordinator*

10) *Practise Karate for one hour this week*

Productivity

Have you ever considered just how much time you really spend working? If you sat down to revise for one hour, how long do you actually spend revising? Do you get up to make coffee, check your texts or emails? Sometimes distractions happen despite your best efforts, such as a phone call from a friend or a family member walks in to have a chat.

Tips to minimise distractions:

- Tidy and organise your study space before you start working, so that you do not waste time looking for things.
- Collect all of the materials that you will need at the very start.
- Close your door and put up a sign to let everyone know that you will be working for the next hour and not to distract you unless it is very important.
- Put your phone on silent.
- De-activate automatic notifications such email, texts and Facebook, which pop up on your computer – or turn your computer screen off.
- Get yourself a drink before you start.
- Clear your desk of magazines or any other items, which might distract you.

It might be a good idea to monitor how much time you actually spend working and identify your biggest distractions. The next time that you plan to sit down and work, use this template to reflect on the experience:

What do you plan to work on? What are your measurable objectives?

How long will you work for?

How many breaks will you have?

What items do you think that you will need? Have you collected these?

Start time: End Time:

Breaks:

Record the start and end times of any interruptions:

How long did you actually spend working?

What could you do next time to minimise the distractions?

How will you improve next time?

Chapter 9: Communicating with Patients

Mentor's Tip

You do not need to know any clinical skills to get into medical school. Superficial knowledge about common medical conditions, or the ABCDE approach might demonstrate insight, but this is not expected of you. One clinical skill that is worth understanding and knowing about however is history taking. Simply being aware of the structure and its significance, can help you to understand what doctors are doing when they communicate with patients. It will also make your work experience a little more interesting. Remember that you are not expected to be a fluent history taker before you get into medicine, but you can demonstrate insight if you know about the process of history taking; essentially a refined method for communicating with patients.

Introduction to History Taking

History taking is a skill that all doctors have to master. It arguably the most frequently used clinical tool. Only through practice will you be able to develop a sharp, thorough and concise interviewing ability. Poor history taking will prevent you from making accurate diagnoses and could even lead to legal action, threatening your medical license and credibility. However, many medical applicants make the mistake of underestimating the difficulty of history taking. It is not enough to simply ask a string of memorised questions; you must be able to interpret the responses and also to pick up on body language cues. Aside from asking the correct questions, you must also develop time management skills. In real life, doctors are expected to thoroughly interview a patient within 10-15 minutes (except for some specialties where histories can take longer e.g. psychiatry). Practising history taking will help to develop your reasoning skills, and to make your questions more precise. This in turn will improve your time management and in turn, the fluidity of your history.

A good history is structured, and basically consists of the following sections:

- Presenting Complaint (PC),
- History of Presenting Complaint (HPC),
- Past Medical/Surgical/Psychiatric History (PMH),
- Drug History (DH) – including medicines, alternative therapies, illegal drugs, prescribed medication...and allergies (to medications and other things).
- Social History (SH) and working history.
- Family History (FH).
- End pieces:
    - Review of systems,
    - summary and questions,
    - differential diagnosis,
    - examination and investigations
    - Referral, safety netting and follow up
    - Management plan

Presenting Complaint (PC)

The PC is arguably the most important component of the history and therefore it is essential to take the time to collate all the relevant pieces of information, to help make your diagnosis. The PC is essentially why the patient has come to see the doctor – a headache, sickness, cancer review or not happy with asthma medication, to name a few. Frustratingly, the presenting complaint does not always match with a patient's 'main complaint', so make sure you ask if there are any other reasons why they are seeing the doctor today.

The PC will give you a good indication of which body systems are affected, and lead your working diagnosis in the right direction. However, it is important not to jump to a premature conclusion, because this can prevent you from considering other possibilities. Remember there are more parts to the history, which may bring up new information; which in turn may point to a more appropriate diagnosis. For this reason, doctors like to use a differential diagnosis system. This is essentially a list of diagnoses that they can be added to, as information presents itself during the history; ranked in order of likeliness, at the end. At this early stage, keeping an open mind is important and helps to ensure that you are thorough in your investigation; casting your net wide for differential diagnoses.

History of the Presenting Complaint (HPC)

The HPC explores the context of the problem, which the patient has initially presented with. It will help to further indicate which body systems are involved. For example, if a patient presents with a cough and breathlessness (the PC), but you learn that these are also associated with recent occasional chest pain, you might consider a cardiovascular problem like angina; instead of a respiratory problem like asthma. If you are being diligent, you might want to note both options down as potential differential diagnoses.

As there is often significant overlap between the PC and the HPC, skilled clinicians will often handle these topics simultaneously. This can be hard to follow on your work experience so listen closely. Fortunately, for PCs that involve pain, there is a really useful mnemonic that can be used to determine the HPC. Pain is also a pretty common PC, for GP, A&E, ward and even community-based patients; you should be able to test this mnemonic out. The HPC mnemonic for pain is **SOCRATES**, which stands for:

Site – where is the pain exactly? Can you point to it? Can you touch it? Deep or superficial?

Onset – when did it (first) start? Do you have it now? When did it stop?

Character – what does it feel like? Can you describe it? Burning, stabbing, aching etc...

Radiation – Does it hurt anywhere else? Does the pain feel like it is moving?

Associated symptoms – Do you have any other symptoms? Think nausea, headache etc.

Timing – How long does it last? Is it constant or episodic? When does it come on?

Exacerbating/alleviating factors – Does anything make it worse/better? Activity or rest?

Severity – on a scale of 1-10 (10 being the worst pain you could experience).

How bad does it feel? Now consider that 10 is unconscious with pain, 1 is imperceptible and 8-9 is breaking a bone – have you broken a bone before? No? What was the worst pain you ever felt? Where you conscious? Yes? That was probably an 8-9 – now how bad is this pain in comparison?

You can do some further reading about SOCRATES online and try a few practice runs with your classmates as mock patients – perhaps in your Medics Society. Remember to practise speaking clearly and helping the conversation to flow; maybe with a bit of humour but you must remain professional. The (very tame) dad-jokes often go down well at interview and are great for developing a rapport with older patients. It is also possible to adapt SOCRATES to complaints other than pain; again do some more reading and think about some other common complaints that might encourage a patient to see their doctor. Remember information that you obtain from patients in the PC and HPC, will indicate the type of questions you will also need to ask, for the later sections of the history.

Past Medical History (PMH)

The PMH can indicate if a previously stable condition has developed into a severe problem. For example a patient with a history of angina could have had a heart attack, or developed heart failure. Previous illnesses can increase the risk of your patient having a particular condition and therefore aid your diagnosis. Relationships between health problems must be investigated, and the implications for your patient must be considered. Often patients with previous problems will have a history of medical visits to the hospital, their GP, or a surgical history. It is useful to enquire about this and it also helps to remind patients of forgotten ailments, which could also be essential to the current diagnosis. For example an incisional hernia may be causing pain in a patient with a history of abdominal surgery. Finally, make sure you ask about past psychiatric illnesses and psychological diagnoses and treatments. These add to the larger picture, and potentially the differential diagnosis.

Drug History (DH)

Taking a DH after a PMH is advised; It not only continues smoothly on from discussing previous medical conditions but also enables you to make links back to the PMH. You can check to see if a patient is taking a drug for a condition that was mentioned in the PMH, and sometimes patients give you names of drugs for conditions they forgot to inform you of earlier. This commonly happens in elderly patients who are on several types of medication, for various health problems; some may not know that they have a condition, or patients otherwise might not consider some health problems important enough to report in the PMH. Examples are mild asthma or anaemia, even though they use inhalers or take iron supplements. When taking a drug history it is important to enquire about:

- The names and dosages of the medicines prescribed to the patient.

- The names and dosages of medicines the patient used in the past.

- Any recent changes in dosages?

- Allergies to any medication or other substances. Also make note of what happens if they come into contact with the allergen e.g. nausea, fits, itching. This is important to distinguish whether a patient is actually allergic to the medication or just experiencing some side effects e.g. weight gain or skin changes with the oral contraceptive pill.

- You should also ask about self-medication with herbal remedies. St John's Wort for example, interacts with many established medications.

- Ask about over the counter medications, as these also have side effects and are often missed. *For example a patient may have stomach ache and forget to tell you that they had several ibuprofen tablets this morning, before breakfast. They may also mention the stomach ache latently as they really came in about a headache and visual disturbance. Incidentally, ibuprofen can damage the lining of an empty stomach – causing stomach ache!*

- Also ask about illegal or illicit drugs, any off-prescription medication or tablets from another country (antibiotics are available without prescription in many countries). N.B. most patients associated the word 'drug' with illegal drugs, so perhaps best to stick with 'medications' instead – unless you mean illegal drugs!

- Finally, do not forget to ask about recently discontinued medication or one off treatments in the past.

Social History (SH)

It is important that you approach this aspect of the history with some caution, and accept that the patient may not want to give you the information that you need to know, or may lie. It is useful to enquire about alcohol consumption and smoking first because it smoothly continues from the drug history – ask about illicit drugs here if you forgot in the DH. Specifically, you need to elicit details of the number of units of alcohol consumed per week and the number of cigarettes smoked in 'pack years'. A pack year is 20 cigarettes smoked per day for a year. If you have not already asked your patient about their occupation, then now is when you should enquire about it. The social history provides a good opportunity to find out about your patient's hobbies and how they spend their free time. This leads in nicely to talking about diet, exercise and other environmental factors at home and at work. Family life should also be explored here, as this can all have an impact upon healthy living. Living alone and being single for a man, is often used as a predictor of poor health later in life.

Next you should try adding to your differential diagnosis. Try linking the SH factors with previous information from the earlier history; to conditions that could be exacerbated by these SH factors. For example, let us say that your patient has reported a poor diet and low exercise tolerance; added to a past medical history of angina, a PC and HPC of recent chest pain and a recent change in anti-angina medication from the DH. He also lives in a third-floor flat, with no lift. The plot thickens and your cardiovascular differentials begin to rise up the list. Do be aware however, that in patients with multiple lifestyle factors and multiple previous medical histories, there could actually be multiple conditions in co-existence. Long-term smokers for example, put themselves at signficicantly increased risk of both respiratory (chronic obstructive pulmonary disease) and cardiovascular (coronary artery and atherosclerotic) diseases.

Being very thorough with SH factors such as smoking, fatty diets, poor exercise, and stress, can really narrow down your options. If there are still equally likely differential diagnosis, try adding a bit of family history to the mix. Remember it could also be more than one disease!

Family History (FH)

The final (main) constituent of a history is the FH. It is important to be accurate and detailed when inquiring about illnesses in the family, even if the topics may be sensitive. Some patients will omit mentioning certain conditions because they do not feel that they are important, or because they themselves have not yet been diagnosed with anything. Therefore, it is often helpful to patients if they are reminded of certain common illnesses, which may be prevalent in the family or in deceased relatives. For this, you can employ the following useful mnemonic:

Just remember **JADE TAB MARCH**:

Jaundice

Anaemia

Diabetes

Emphysema

Tuberculosis/Transient Ischemic Attack (TIA or mini stroke)

Asthma

Bronchitis

Myocardial Infarction

Angina

Rheumatic fever

Congestive Heart Failure/Cancer/Cardiovascular Accident (CVA or stroke)

Hypertension

You should make a note of which family members had which conditions; what age they developed or contracted them and whether they are still alive. Also double check for actual blood relationships; some people have differing opinions as to what constitutes family – an uncle or aunt might only be related by marriage, for example. FH can provide some cues to diagnosis, independently of the preceding history, but is can also mislead. For example, if a (blood related) aunt developed breast cancer at the age of 70, this is not necessarily a positive family history for breast cancer. The risk is certainly increased however, if the aunt developed it when she was younger than 50 years of age. Similarly, a positive family history may provide a link to the system that has been affected – not necessarily the same medical condition. For example, a patient with ulcerative colitis may have had a father who suffered from Crohn's disease.

Although there may be a positive family history, you should regard this initially as a risk factor and not confirmation that your patient has the same disease (with a few exceptions). Remember, you have to look at the patient as a whole (cue holistic care), and you will probably have to do some further investigations anyway, such as blood tests or a CT scan.

Medicine is all about asking questions and gathering information. On this note, you will most likely have to speak to colleagues; refer your patient to a specialist or even attend a multidisciplinary team (MDT) meeting, to get a whole range of inputs (far beyond your medical remit – but important to be aware of for future everyday practice).

End Pieces *(Review of systems; summary and questions; examination and investigations; referral, safety netting and follow up; differential diagnosis management plan).* At the end of the medical history, there are several things that efficient clinicians do to make sure they have all of the information available:

The **review of systems** or a 'head-to-toe' check, is a way of asking about any other commons symptoms, which the patient may have forgotten to mention. This helps to jog their memory and potentially give additional clues as to the diagnosis and management, or the need for further investigations. Employing this approach is safe, thorough and efficient – all good attributes to demonstrate in a medical interview.

The **summary and questions,** are opportunities to double check all of the events communicated by the patient; to allow them to fill in any gaps, and to make sure the clinician has not missed anything or detailed something incorrectly. Again, this information helps to direct the diagnosis, management, further tests or the need for specialist referral. Summarising looks really slick in an interview and asking questions shows that you are actively listening to the patient...and being extra safe – all good stuff to demonstate!

Examinations and investigations are used to confirm or rule out differential diagnosis. Often they lead to further tests, observation or specialist referral. Sometimes individual test results can be very telling, such as a mass on a scan. At other times, a series of tests is needed to create a clearer picture. For example blood sugars and HbA1C testing in diabetes. Having a good insight into available tests that are relevant to your differential diagnosis, demonstrates that you have really learnt something from your work experience.

Referral, safety netting and follow up are ways of maintaining communication with patients. They allow for further testing and monitoring of chronic conditions. They are also a good way of encouraging patients with high risk conditions, such as HIV or obesity, to seek treatment and/or make lifestyle changes. Talking about safety netting and follow up in an MMI station or medical panel interview, is a great way of communicating realistic insight into the everyday workings of the NHS. Referring a patient on, demonstrates understanding of the limitations of certain medical fields (such as general practice), and how the wider NHS system essentially works together, as one big team.

The **differential diagnosis** lists of all of the conditions, diseases or syndromes you think the patient might have. Order them in terms of which is most likely. These can then be discussed with a supervisor, so you can share your thought processes. You may be asked what you think the diagnosis is in a medical interview. You are not really expected to have detailed medical knowledge, but you can apply some of your insight and wider reading knowledge, to the situation. Making a diagnosis with a logical justification (from the history), demonstrates excellent problem solving ability – a key transferrable skill for medicine.

The **management plan** is essentially what you would do next. It carries on from the differential diagnosis and technically includes all of the end pieces mentioned above. The management plan is flexible, adaptable in response to new information or results, and different for every case (patient/person). You may be asked what you would do in an interview situation, where the diagnosis is unsure or there is a risk to the patient and the public. The answer to this question will require you to apply some logical thought processes, regarding further investigation, specialist referral, safety netting and additional counselling of the patient.

During your work experience, pay careful attention to how doctors conclude consultations and what they do if things are not clear; speak to the doctor about what is going to happen to their patient now. For the purposes of an interview situation, you have to make sure the mock patient is happy and safe. You may also be asked to process ethical and medico legal concerns, by the invigilator. Make sure you review the relevant chapters in this book, before your interview.

History taking pro forma (do not record or remove any patient identifying data!)

On the next page there is a history taking pro forma, which you can use on your work experience when speaking to patients. There is a very serious caveat to its use however: you are not allowed to take patient identifying data out of the ward or clinic, so do not write down any names or addresses - simply use letters instead. For example Mrs X. Even in this case however, a patient could still be identified from circumstantial details alone. It is imperative therefore, that you discuss using a history taking pro forma, with your supervisor on the ward; make sure they are satisfied that you have no personal identifying information in anything that you remove from the clinical zone.

You may find that doctors are happy for you to record your notes (using the history subheadings), on a separate piece of paper, so that you can present a case to them. They may then ask you to put this in confidential waste before you leave the ward/surgery. In this case, you have learnt from the process even if you do not have the notes to review later. Remember the ethical need for confidentiality, the potential harm to patients from breaching this, and the NHS's responsibilities under the Data Protection Act 1998, to maintain written information securely.

Medical History Pro Forma

Patient demographics		**Examples:** Age, gender etc. Do not record any patient-identifying information i.e. name, address etc. Check with your supervisor if unsure!
Presenting complaint (PC)		**Examples:** Pain, nausea, vomiting What is their main complaint? Is it different to the PC?
History of presenting complaint (HPC)		**Examples:** See above SOCRATES for pain, can be adapted to other PC's
Past medical history (PMH), Past surgical history (PSH), Past psychiatric history (PPH)		**Examples:** Previous heart attack, previous hernia operation, previous diagnosis and treatment for depression.
Drug history (DH) and allergies		**Examples:** Statin for high cholesterol, blood pressure or diabetes medication, allergic to penicillin (anaphylaxis) and pollen (sneezing only)
Social history (SH) Smoking (pack years), diet, exercise, work, home & social life		**Examples:** Lives in a two-story house with no stair-lift, works as a retail assistant, does less than 30 minutes of strenuous exercise per week, like curry & chips a lot! 25 pack years!
Family history (FH)		**Examples:** Any blood relatives who had diseases or health problems? Are their family still alive? What did they die of and when? Be compassionate!
End pieces: Review of systems, summary and questions, examinations and investigations, referral/safety-netting/follow up, differential diagnosis & management plan		**Examples:** Anything else you want to ask the patient? Do you need more information? How would you get this? Who else would you involve? What is the likely diagnosis? What are you going to do about it?

Conclusion

There is a lot of new information contained within this text. It is probably wise to review specific chapters repeatedly. Not only has this knowledge improved your insight into medicine, but you can now make stronger medical links in your personal statement, and provide accurate logical answers in the interview. If there are topics that you are struggling with, you can attend Medic Mentor's Summer School; to provide comprehensive personal statement tutoring and interview preparation. Alternatively, if you just have a question or two, you can drop us a message via email or arrange a free telephone consultation with a Mentor. We will always try our best to assist you.

Not all students will have taken the time and energy to complete reading such a comprehensive text as this, so you should be congratulated on your achievement. Be sure to spend some time researching some of the topics in the first few chapters, in more detail. Combining this knowledge with Medic Mentor's other medical application guides, will be extremely beneficial to you. Don't forget to check out the *Personal Statement Toolkit* and the *Interview Skills Checklist* books, available from *www.MedicMentor.co.uk*

Well done, and we wish you the best of luck with your medical school applications!

Keep in touch,

Medic Mentor

Further Reading

1. Strathern P. A Brief History of Medicine, From Hippocrates to Gene Therapy. Constable & Robinson; 2005.

2. Hope RA. Medical Ethics: A Very Short Introduction. Oxford University Press; 2004.

3. Bynum W. The History of Medicine: A Very Short Introduction. Oxford University Press; 2008.

4. NHS values in action and making a difference. NHS England. Available from: https://www.england.nhs.uk/2014/02/nhs-values-in-action/

5. Data Protection Act. 1998. Legislation.gov.uk. Available at: http://www.legislation.gov.uk/ukpga/1998/29/pdfs/ukpga_19980029_en.pdf

6. Mental Health Act. 1983. Legislation.gov.uk. Available at: http://www.legislation.gov.uk/ukpga/1983/20/pdfs/ukpga_19830020_en.pdf

7. Employment Rights Act 1996. Legislation.gov.uk. Available at: https://www.legislation.gov.uk/ukpga/1996/18/contents

8. Good Medical Practice. General Medical Council. Available at: http://www.gmc-uk.org/guidance/good_medical_practice.asp

9. Outcomes for graduates (originally published in Tomorrow's Doctors 2009). Available from: inhttps://www.gmc-uk.org/education/standards-guidance-and-curricula/standards-and-outcomes/outcomes-for-graduates

10. NHS Improvement. Website homepage. Available from: https://improvement.nhs.uk

11. National Institute for Clinical Excellence (NICE). Website homepage. Available from: www.nice.org.uk

12. British Medical Association (BMA). Website homepage. Available from: www.bma.org.uk

13. The new junior doctors' contract and their reaction. Available from Full Fact. Freely accessible at the following URL: https://fullfact.org/health/new-junior-doctors-contract-and-their-reaction/

14. The Nuffield Trust. The NHS workforce in numbers. Freely available online at the following URL: https://www.nuffieldtrust.org.uk/resource/the-nhs-workforce-in-numbers

15. GDPR. Information Commissioner's Office. Available from: https://ico.org.uk/for-organisations/guide-to-the-general-data-protection-regulation-gdpr/

16. Brief guide: capacity and competence in under 18s. Care Quality Commission. Available from: https://www.cqc.org.uk/sites/default/files/20180228_briefguide-capacity_consent_under_18s_v2.pdf

17. Nigel's suergery 8: Gillick competency and Fraser guidelines. Care Quality Commission. Available from: https://www.cqc.org.uk/guidance-providers/gps/nigels-surgery-8-gillick-competency-fraser-guidelines

18. How is the NHS structured? The King's Fund. Available from: https://www.kingsfund.org.uk/audio-video/how-new-nhs-structured

19. Greenhalgh T. How to Read a Paper: The Basics of Evidence-Based Medicine. Wiley Blackwell; 5th Edition, 2014.

20. Cottrell S. Palgrave Study Skills: The Study Skills Handbook. Palgrave MacMillan; 4th Edition, 2013.